*electrons
on the move*

electrons

A Westinghouse Search Book

on the move

by Scientists of the Westinghouse
Research Laboratories

ALLAN BENNETT
ROBERT HEIKES
PAUL KLEMENS
ALEXEI MARADUDIN
SHARON BANIGAN, *Executive Editor*

WALKER AND COMPANY
NEW YORK

Already published in this series:

THE SCIENCE OF SCIENCE
ENERGY DOES MATTER

Contents

APPENDIX

Foreword

THE VITALITY of civilization depends upon the integration of all creative endeavor. It is, therefore, a cause for deep concern that modern society fosters specialism and segregation.

Scientists, like other specialists, are segregated from those in other fields by the restrictive boundaries of their several areas of science. Each is able to comprehend but a little of the rapidly increasing vastness of scientific knowledge. Nevertheless, scientists know from experience that the discovery of knowledge in one area of science often depends on familiarity with many other fields of science; so also does the application of science to useful ends. And they have reasonable faith in the unity of science. Accordingly, preparation for a successful career in research or teaching should include the study of many related fields of science.

Scientists face the more difficult challenge of communicating to laymen the objectives and methods of science and sufficient scientific knowledge so that those who are not scientists may live intelligently in a civilization based on science and technology. Unless this is done, the great majority of people will be unwitting pawns of forces they do not comprehend. The alternatives to wider, greater understanding of science among all people are repugnant: a society divided between those who understand the forces which mold their lives and those who are ignorant, or suppression of curiosity which is the motive of research. The former could lead to social chaos, the latter opposes the spirit of man who is "that one of God's creatures who has the power of understanding."

The challenge of which I have spoken is made more formidable by rapidly accumulating scientific knowledge recorded so that it can be understood only by a few. The reason was stated by the authors of the first volume in this series: "No single event will characterize the present century as much as the accelerating pace of its research activity and the technology that has followed from it." Many predict that new discoveries of scientific knowledge of living things and the universe in which they live will exceed in the next fifty years all man's previous discoveries throughout his long evolution.

I am not dismayed by the magnitude of the challenge. Mastery of electrons, which are the subject of this volume, has given us new means for communicating knowledge and ideas. Electronic devices have extended the range of the human mind's power of memory, computation and thought. I am heartened by the fact that many of our graduate schools and industrial laboratories stress the ancient ideal of an educated man: "to know everything about something and something about everything." And I am reminded by this book that scientists can and do write not so they can be understood, but so that they cannot be misunderstood.

And so, I judge *Electrons on the Move* to be significant for three among many reasons. It communicates knowledge and understanding of science with clarity to those who are not scientific specialists. It recounts the sequence of scientific discoveries that have given man power to control electrons for the limitless uses of man. It reveals the relations of sectors of science separated by unnatural barriers of specialism and thus stresses the unity of natural knowledge.

DETLEV W. BRONK
President of The Rockefeller Institute
Past President of the National Academy of Sciences

PART

1

Ground Rules

Satellite Mariner II as it appeared in space. Over-all height: 8 feet. The two wing-like planes on either side are banks of solar cells which power the satellite's instruments and transmitters. The dish-shaped structure at bottom is the directional antenna used for long-range communication with Earth.

Mariner
and Method

THROUGH THE LONELY blackness of space, a weird craft coasts in free fall toward its destination—a cloud-covered planet shrouded in mystery. Launched nearly four months and a hundred million miles before, this ship had corrected the error in its original course at a command from its makers, transmitted when it was but a million and a half miles from home. Now, inanimate yet sentient, it is about to begin the first examination ever made at close range of a planet whose invisible surface has so far defied observation. What will it find?

The craft is space probe Mariner II, launched from Cape Kennedy (formerly Canaveral), Florida, on August 27, 1962. On September fourth its course was corrected in response to a radio command from the earth, which placed the vessel on a path that would carry it to within twenty-two thousand miles of Venus with an accuracy comparable to sending an arrow through a melon a mile away. From this vantage point, Mariner II observed the planet on December fourth with an ease that earthbound astronomers can only envy. The results, transmitted to earth—then thirty-six million miles away—set a new record for long-distance radio communication.

In the launching, course correction, and the collection and transmission of data, this triumph of space technology vividly illustrates several aspects of the science of electrons on the move. An understanding of this science is essential not only to the development of such advanced systems as Mariner II, but to the comprehension of a multitude of devices and phenomena such as automotive ignition systems, fluorescent lights, transistors, cyclotrons, lightning, auroras, and corrosion, to name but a few. Indeed, since electrons and electric charge are a fundamental part of all matter, an understanding of the interactions of electric charge is a necessary prelude to any detailed understanding of nature.

Why should we want to understand nature? The answer to this question, just as the answer to why we should want to send a Mariner to study Venus, is "Because it's there." Throughout the history of humanity, the urge to understand the unknown has been of itself a dominant factor. To be sure, there is also a more practical consideration: Any improvement in our understanding of the behavior of nature is almost certain to increase our ability to control that behavior, to make us that much more her master than her slave.

We will focus our attention primarily on the role of the mobile electron as a carrier of electric current. But we must bear in mind that the electron also serves another essential function as one of the building blocks of all matter.

It is now well established that matter consists of individual—but no longer indivisible—units called atoms. For many purposes, each atom may be visualized as a miniature solar system, mostly empty space except for one or more electrons revolving in closed orbits around a massive, charged nucleus, much as planets revolve about the sun. Just as most of the total mass of the solar system is found in the sun, so most of the mass of the atom is concentrated in the nucleus. Atoms of different chemical elements differ in the number of their planetary electrons, and correspondingly in the mass and the charge of their nuclei. Situations occur, either natural or man-made, in which an atom, or a group of atoms—a molecule—is temporarily made to gain or lose one or more of its electrons, and this results in a charged structure called an *ion*. Examples of the ionic state are furnished by most of the common salts, including table salt.

Whenever we try to explain new and strange phenomena, we tend quite naturally to point out similarities to known phenomena, as we did in describing an atom in the more familiar terms of the solar sys-

tem. However, it is almost always impossible to explain atomic behavior accurately by scaling down a description that applies to systems
large enough to be seen by the naked eye, because the concepts used
for such *macroscopic* systems can be misleading when applied to
microscopic events.

Let's think for a moment about the familiar ideas of color and size,
for example. Objects large enough to be seen by the naked eye usually
have a fairly definite color, which can be evaluated with reasonable
accuracy either visually or by using optical instruments. In such cases
we can state, "This object has a specific color," and this can be taken
to mean, "All experiments or observations made to determine the
color of this object will have identical results." But the first statement
is useful only to the extent that the second holds true. This concept of
color is convenient and appropriate in describing macroscopic objects,
but the color of an atom or an electron has little significance, because
such particles are so small compared to the wavelengths of visible
light that they do not reflect light at all in the usual sense.

We may think that when we come to size we are on safer ground,
and this is true to a certain extent. There can be little question about
the size of a billiard ball, for example. We know that we can measure
its size quite precisely using a caliper, a micrometer, or even a ruler.
But such precision is possible only because the ball has a sharply
defined surface boundary and we feel quite certain that we know
when the caliper or the micrometer touches that surface. On the
other hand, if we try to measure a cloud with similar methods we are
obviously in trouble. Even someone in an airplane traveling through
a cloud is unable to tell precisely where it begins and ends. In other
words, it is impossible to specify the size of an object, however easily
visible it may be, unless the positions of its boundaries can be accurately defined and measured.

It is true that the sizes of atoms and molecules can be determined
with fair accuracy, but difficulties arise when we try to measure the
size of an electron. Direct measurement with an instrument such as a
micrometer is obviously out of the question even in principle. Assuming it were possible to devise such an instrument, its very atomic nature would insure its consisting mostly of empty space far larger than
the electron to be measured. In any event, it is difficult at present to
conceive of any experimental method of determining the size of the

electron. About all we can say is that an electron appears to be no larger than about 10^{-13} centimeters.*

Another example shows how inadequate macroscopic ideas can be when applied to the atomic scale. It concerns the question of whether electrons (and also light) consist of particles or waves. Conventionally, we think of sand as composed of small particles or grains. Early atomic theory was successful in suggesting that such grains could be subdivided into molecules, which in turn could be divided into atoms, then electrons, protons, and perhaps other constituents, too. It was tempting to treat each of these subdivisions as collections of small hard particles similar to miniature billiard balls. Sound, on the other hand, had long been recognized as a wave phenomenon, and very adequately explained by extensive mathematical study of wave motion. The two concepts, particle and wave, appeared to describe entirely different things—one a kind of matter, the other a kind of motion. Sound and sand, wave and particle; how could they be confused? Yet experiments showed that light, and later electrons, cannot be said to be either wave or particle, because each has some of the properties of both waves and particles. To say that an electron *is* a wave or a particle or something else is meaningful only in so far as it agrees with the results of experiment. If no experiment can be devised whose results depend on a supposed characteristic of the electron, it is meaningless to say that the electron has that characteristic. For example, in the following chapters we will make no reference to the size of an electron, because no experimental way of measuring such a size appears to be known. It is probably safe to assume that an electron is smaller than, say, 10^{-13} centimeters in diameter, but aside from this limitation the electron cannot be said to *have* a size. On the other hand, both the mass and the charge of an electron can be accurately defined by experiment, and therefore it is meaningful to say that an electron has mass and charge.

These examples illustrate some of the pitfalls encountered in applying macroscopic concepts to atomic systems, and demonstrate the necessity of experimental observability as a criterion for judging the pertinence of a concept.

---

* Very large numbers or very small numbers are often conveniently written in this exponential notation. Ten, with a positive exponent n, for example, is shorthand for the number 1 followed by n zeros. A negative exponent denotes the reciprocal of the preceding number, or a decimal point followed by $n - 1$ zeros and a one.

In discussing the laws that govern electron motion, we will naturally explain ideas in words, but we will also find it convenient at times to use mathematical description in terms of equations. Why is this necessary or desirable? The answer to this question is by no means trivial and, since it applies to science in general, let's digress a moment to discuss it.

An essential part of a scientific understanding of any phenomenon is the ability to describe it quantitatively, that is, in numbers that tell *how much* happens, in contrast to a qualitative description that only says in a general way *what* happens, without specifying how much. An equation is basically a shorthand notation that states the procedure we can use, when the circumstances of any given problem are known, to calculate numerical values for the quantities that are of interest. Although such a procedure can be expressed in words, it is invariably stated more compactly and elegantly in mathematical symbolism, that is, in an equation. This conciseness alone might justify the use of equations, but there are, in fact, much more important advantages in store.

First, the solution of physical problems usually requires considering several processes that interact simultaneously. Even if each process might be completely, if clumsily, describable in words, it is not at all clear how to combine the various descriptions to derive a single one expressing the over-all result. However, written as equations, these descriptions can be combined and manipulated by a set of rules we call algebra, which is only a formalized combination of the familiar operations of addition, subtraction, multiplication, and division. By means of such combinations we eventually construct an equation expressing the relations between the known quantities and the unknown ones we want to find. Thus, the language of mathematics provides a systematic procedure for the solution of physical problems. We might add that the success of these techniques in solving such problems has inspired the development of arithmetic treatments of other kinds of problems, normally thought to be logical rather than mathematical. The resulting symbolic logic has been an essential tool in the design of switching circuits and computers.

Another advantage is that direct inspection of an equation shows both the way and the amount in which the quantities of interest will be affected by changes in the conditions of the problem. For instance, we can see how to choose or alter the starting conditions to make the results those we want. In short, the use of equations can save time and effort.

In choosing mathematical symbols, the scientist tries to avoid the confusion of duplication, but he soon exhausts the letters of the English alphabet and resorts to the Greek. The use of Greek symbols for certain specific quantities is now well established; we will simply continue the custom. For purposes of identification, the Greek alphabet is listed in the Appendix, under the heading of "Certain Symbols." We will try to avoid using the same symbol for different quantities; if at times this is unavoidable, we will call attention to it.

We are going to explore the properties of electrons, both free and in matter, with particular emphasis on vacuum tubes and solid-state devices. We will also review some of the history of the electron and the scientific detective work that uncovered its well-kept secrets. And finally, we will discuss some recent developments, such as lasers and photoelectric image tubes.

2

Portrait
of a Charge

WE START WITH the electron itself. What is it? Ultimately, the definition must be given in terms of the results of experimental measurements. We will describe some of these experiments later, but first let's consider a few experimental results that support our concept of the electron.

We can think of the electron as a very small, indivisible, fundamental entity—for our purposes we might cautiously say "particle"—a major constituent of all matter. All electrons appear to be identical and to have properties that do not change with time. Two essential attributes of the electron are its mass and its charge. Qualitatively, we can think of an electron as "a piece of matter" that has weight and is affected by gravity. Just as the mass of any object is defined, we can define the mass of the electron by applying a force and measuring the resulting rate of change in the velocity of the electron, that is, the rapidity with which its velocity changes. This rate of change is called the *acceleration*, and the electron mass is then defined as the ratio of the applied force to the resulting acceleration. If the force is expressed in *dynes* (a pound weight is roughly half a million dynes) and the acceleration is given in cm/sec^2, then the mass—the quotient of these—is expressed in grams. (On the earth's surface a mass of 29 grams weighs about one ounce.) It is found that the mass of the electron is about 9.11×10^{-28} grams. Not only the electron but all matter appears to have positive mass, which is equivalent to saying that a force applied to any object results in an acceleration in the same direction as the force.

How does the other aspect, the charge of the electron, arise? Between any two pieces of matter in their ordinary state, there will be a force of attraction equal to a constant, times the product of the masses of the two pieces, divided by the square of the distance between them. This is the well-known Law of Universal Gravitation, proposed by Sir Isaac Newton. This force holds the atmosphere, us, and our environment to the earth, and in turn it holds the earth in orbit about the sun. It is important to note that the constant we have referred to is the same for *any* two pieces of matter, whatever they may be. Now, it is an observed fact that if two suitably chosen pieces of matter, such as a piece of wool and a piece of glass, are rubbed together and then separated, the attractive force between them is much greater than the gravitational force that existed before rubbing. It cannot reasonably be supposed that the rubbing has increased the mass of either object, particularly since the weight of each, or the gravitational force between it and the earth, shows no measurable change. Furthermore, two pieces of wool or of glass treated in this way will repel each other with a force exceeding the gravitational attraction. To try to explain this on a gravitational basis would require assuming that one of the masses—but *only* one— has been made negative by the rubbing. However, weighing still shows both masses to be positive and unchanged.

This state of affairs can be explained by assuming that all matter is made up of various combinations of several kinds of identical building blocks, or fundamental particles. In addition to their mass, some of these particles have something we call *electric charge,* or *quantity of electricity.* We attribute the following properties to this charge:

1. There are two types of electric charge, arbitrarily called *positive* and *negative.*
2. Between any two bodies each having a *net* excess of charge of *like* sign, there will be a repulsive force proportional to the product of the amounts of excess charge, divided by the square of the distance between the bodies.

3. Between any two bodies having net charges of *unlike* sign or type, there will be an attractive force similarly dependent on charge and distance.

When we speak of the charge of a body, we almost always mean the *net* charge, the difference between the total amounts of positive and negative charge contained in the body.

On the basis of these three properties, we explain the results of rubbing wool against glass in the following way: Before rubbing, the wool had equal amounts of evenly distributed charge of both types, and so did the glass. Therefore, any attractive forces between the particles of unlike charge on each object was balanced by repulsive forces between like charges, so that all forces due to the charges exactly canceled, leaving only gravitational forces. We suppose that during the rubbing some of the particles of one sign were "rubbed off" one object onto the other, leaving a net excess of one kind of charge on one object, and thus a net excess of the opposite charge on the other. The result is an attractive force between unlike charges, as observed. Two pieces of wool or of glass, similarly rubbed, will each have net excesses of the same type of charge, and therefore there will be a repulsive force between them, again in agreement with observation.

If we investigate further, we find that all electrons have an electric charge, and the amount of charge, like the mass, is identical for all electrons. No one has ever succeeded in isolating an amount of charge smaller than that of the electron. Furthermore, all amounts of charge of either type that can be isolated appear to be exact integral multiples of the electron charge. In other words, charge seems to come in discrete units—atoms of electricity, as it were—equal in magnitude to the electron charge. The sign of the charge of the electron is conventionally defined as negative; the electron thus represents the fundamental unit of negative charge.

No experiment yet devised has succeeded in removing the charge from the electron, leaving only its mass. Therefore, instead of considering the electron a "massive" body that has somehow acquired a charge, it seems more realistic to think that the electron *is* the charge, and that the charge and the mass are two inseparable aspects of a single entity. To be sure, there are other fundamental particles with mass and with charge—positive, negative, or zero—but these

This group of four photographs shows a superconducting magnet, a recent development in the production of intense magnetic fields. Here the phenomenon of superconductivity, the complete absence of electrical resistivity in certain metals at temperatures near absolute zero, is utilized to permit very large currents to flow without heat generation or power loss. This magnet can produce magnetic fields of 90,000 gauss within the one-inch-diameter central hole; to produce such fields without superconductivity requires about a million watts of electrical power, and thousands

(Westinghouse Research Laboratory)

of gallons of cooling water per minute. The superconducting magnet, on the other hand, requires only a relatively modest refrigerating installation in order to maintain its coils within a few degrees of absolute zero, or $-273°C$ ($-459°F$). The sample in the central hole need not be so cold; its temperature will be prescribed by the experiment being performed. The last photo in this group shows a superconducting magnet through whose center passes a plasma jet at several thousand degrees, emerging white-hot from the tailpiece below.

charges are always integral multiples, usually unity, of the electron charge. One of these particles, the *positron*, has a unit positive charge and about the same mass as the electron; it is often regarded as the fundamental unit of positive charge.

In practice, the net charge on a macroscopic body is always extremely small compared to the total number of positive and negative charges which together make up the body, although it can be very much larger than the charge of one electron; the net charge can be either positive, negative, or zero. This net charge is always observed to be an integral multiple of the electron charge. From this it follows that the magnitudes of the fundamental units of positive and negative charge are identical to a surprising degree of precision. Let's see why this is so. For the sake of argument, suppose that the charge q_e of the electron *did* exceed the charge q_p of the positron by one part in a million, that is, $q_e = 1.000001 \, q_p$. We might expect that such a very small discrepancy could easily be overlooked. But how would this minute difference affect, for example, a body containing 500,000 hydrogen atoms, that is, 500,000 electrons and 500,000 protons? (The proton charge appears identical to that of the positron.) We see that such a body—very roughly one millionth of a millionth of a millionth of a gram—would then have a net excess of negative charge of half an electron charge, and thus bodies of visible size would show a wide range of fractional net charges. Yet the experimental evidence is that there are no such fractional net charges. This can only be explained on the basis of equality of the magnitudes of positive and negative unit charges to a precision greater than the reciprocal of the total number of charges in the bodies involved, say to one part in 10^{20} or so.

The apparent absolute equality of these charge magnitudes is an interesting puzzle, because there is no obvious reason why this should be. Yet it seems unlikely that such identicality is just a coincidence. In this connection, the British physicist P. A. M. Dirac has proposed a theory in which, broadly speaking, all space—even "empty" space— is assumed permeated by a uniform sea of electrons of negative energy. A positron is interpreted as a vacancy or deficiency of one electron in this sea, so the equality of charge is to be expected in this view. It will be fascinating to see how this experimental observation fits future developments of theory.

The magnitude of the electronic charge is most readily described by reference to an electric current, which we can consider simply a flow of charge. The unit of electric current, the *ampere*—about the same as the current in a 100-watt light bulb—represents a flow of a *coulomb* of charge per second. A coulomb is an amount of charge of 6.28×10^{18} electrons, so the electronic charge is 1.59×10^{-19} coulombs. Unfortunately, the sign of the electronic charge was chosen as negative long before it was realized that a flow of electrons is an electric current. As a result, the direction conventionally designated as that of positive current flow, or the flow of positive charge, is opposite to that in which the electrons that normally carry the current actually move.

Electric currents may either be carried by a flow or migration of electrons through matter, as in a wire, or else electrons may be extracted from matter into a surrounding vacuum, which results in a flow of "bare" electrons in the vacuum, and this also constitutes an electric current. We will be dealing later with both of these situations. Electric current may also be carried by flows of other charged particles or complexes, such as a current of positive or negative ions in an electrolyte, or a current of positive "holes" in a semiconductor. Indeed, in some circumstances electric currents may exist, as in radio waves, even in the absence of free charges. In the cases we will discuss, it is generally adequate to consider the electron as a discrete particle. However, as we have already implied, this concept is not to be taken as ultimate reality, because electron diffraction experiments have shown that electrons have some of the properties not only of particles but of waves, too.

The motion of an electron, like that of any other body, results from a force acting on it. How can force be applied to an electron? One way is by gravity. Another is to bring a second charge near the electron, thus exerting an attractive or a repulsive force on it. In this case, we say that the second charge sets up an *electric field* which applies a force to the first charge. Finally, we find that an electric current flow will affect the motion of a nearby charge, but only if that charge is already in motion. In this case, we say that the current sets up a *magnetic field* which applies a force to the moving charge. These three are the only known ways of applying force to an electron. The relationships between these fields, the charges producing them, and the resulting effects on other charges are the laws of electron motion.

Since the forces of gravity are usually insignificant compared to the others, at least in terrestrial experiments, we will consider only the forces exerted by magnetic or electric fields.

When treating the behavior of electrons in matter, we could in principle use the same rules that will be derived for the behavior of individual "free" electrons in a vacuum, but we would then be faced with the irksome necessity of including the effects on the electron of all the charges composing the matter. It is often possible to avoid this complexity by averaging the effects of all these charges and expressing their result as a new or different property, *which we now ascribe to the electron when in matter.* For example, when an electric field is applied to a conductor, the mobile electrons in it move as a result of the total forces applied to them, not only those from the external field but also those from the nearby internal charges. Depending on the particular problem, we may account for the latter by assuming that the only force is from the external field but that the electron has an *effective mass* different from that of a free electron, or that it has a *mobility,* which will be defined later, a property not at all applicable to free electrons. For this reason, the properties ascribed to electrons in matter, or *bound electrons,* may differ from those of free electrons in a vacuum.

Earlier in our discussion, we spoke of understanding the laws of electron motion. What do we mean by understanding? In this sense, it means formulating a theory of electron behavior which explains adequately, but not necessarily exactly, the behavior in cases observed so far, and which hopefully will not only suggest still-untried experiments but will predict results that agree with observation. Failing the latter, we must revise the theory to fit the facts, both old and new. Among otherwise equally adequate theories, the simplest is generally preferable, but the absolute "rightness" of a theory is usually a meaningless and dangerous snare, because it may be upset at any moment by new data.

The understanding we will seek in the following chapters is adequate in the light of present knowledge and for the problems at hand, but it is hardly advisable to consider our theories as fundamental truth. It should be pointed out that we take on faith, with no real justification other than its historical success, that the laws of nature, including those of electron motion, remain constant from one time to another. We are fortunate indeed that electrons all behave identically in endless repetition.

So far we have only a tantalizing glimpse of the electron and the wide variety of ways in which it behaves. Before we investigate this fundamental particle in more detail and discuss the diverse role it plays in our lives, we are going to retrace the steps that first led to its discovery.

3

The Case of
the Elusive Electron

ALTHOUGH PRIMITIVE MAN was familiar with electricity in the form of lightning, he believed it was only one of many awesome manifestations of the supernatural. Centuries before the birth of Christ, the Greeks discovered that amber rubbed with a soft cloth had the power to attract light objects, but they could find no explanation for this phenomenon. About the same time, Greek philosophers were beginning to speculate about the nature of the world in which they lived. Anaxagoras (500–428 B.C.) claimed that matter was capable of being subdivided indefinitely. But just a few years later, Democritus (460–370 B.C.) held that if one continued the subdivision of matter far enough, eventually one would come upon elementary particles that could not be further divided. He called these particles *atomos,* meaning indivisible. Democritus is usually credited with having originated the idea of the atomicity of matter.

That there might be a connection between electricity and the atomicity of matter seems not to have occurred to anyone until more than two thousand years later. The discovery that there is a lower limit to the amount of electricity that can occur in nature, which we now call the electron, and that the electron is an important constituent of the elementary atoms, was made as the nineteenth century ended.

This ultimate triumph of classical or Newtonian physics provided the key to the explanation of the properties of the various elements. It revolutionized the science of chemistry and contributed to the beginnings of solid state physics. But classical physics proved incapable of dealing with the problems presented by its new child, the electron. As the twentieth century opened, classical physics began to be replaced by a new kind, called *quantum* physics.

The story of the search for the electron is interesting for several reasons. To describe this period is to illustrate the international character of science. Physicists from England, France, Germany, and the United States were engaged in a common endeavor, working independently but building on the successes and the failures of their predecessors. The discovery of the electron coincided historically with the end of the unchallenged supremacy of classical physics. In fact, the electron contributed to the end of an era by posing new questions for which classical physics could provide no adequate answers; it was also indirectly responsible for the ultimate ascendancy of quantum physics. Therefore, the story of its discovery also serves as an introduction to the quantum theory.

Several of the many experiments that were carried out over the eighty-year span of the search are now regarded as classics of experimental physics. Yet the ideas underlying these experiments are so simple that anyone even slightly familiar with the principles of physics can understand them.

Although the search for the electron is generally conceded to have started in the 1830's with the researches of the great British experimental physicist Michael Faraday, we begin our story some fifty years earlier.

In 1781, the English chemist Henry Cavendish, while experimenting with the combustion of hydrogen in air and in oxygen, established the fact that the combustion of two volumes of hydrogen in one volume of oxygen yielded water. Then in 1805, the French chemist Joseph Gay-Lussac extended Cavendish's results, and showed that when two volumes of hydrogen combined with one of oxygen exactly two volumes of water vapor were formed. He demonstrated further that one volume of hydrogen combined with one volume of chlorine to produce two volumes of gaseous hydrogen chloride. Generalizing these results, Gay-Lussac concluded that whenever two gases whose volumes bear a simple whole number relation to each other combine, the volume of the resulting product also bears a simple whole number relation to the volumes of the combining gases, provided all measurements are made at the same temperature and pressure.

In explanation of this result it was suggested that equal volumes of all gases, at the same temperature and pressure, contain the same number of atoms. However, it was quickly realized that this could not be the case. If it were, then the combination of two volumes of hydrogen with one volume of oxygen to form two volumes of water vapor would imply that each oxygen atom split itself in two. But this conclusion could not be correct, since it contradicted the accepted idea of an unsplittable atom as the building block of the chemical elements.

The way out of this dilemma was provided in 1811 by the Italian chemist Amadeo Avogadro, who propounded the hypothesis which now bears his name: Equal volumes of all gases at the same temperature and pressure contain the same number of molecules. By "molecule" Avogadro meant a group of atoms, the number of atoms in the group being characteristic of the particular element or compound under consideration. For example, if it were assumed that hydrogen gas is composed of molecules containing two hydrogen atoms each, and similarly for oxygen gas, then according to Avogadro's hypothesis $2n$ molecules of hydrogen gas combine with n molecules of oxygen gas to form $2n$ molecules of water vapor, each oxygen molecule splitting into two oxygen atoms during the combination. This process consists of four hydrogen atoms combining with two oxygen atoms to form two molecules of water, each molecule of water being composed of two hydrogen atoms and one oxygen atom. In the same way, the formation of gaseous hydrogen chloride can be understood if it is assumed that chlorine gas is made up of molecules, each containing two atoms, while gaseous hydrogen chloride is composed of molecules, each consisting of one hydrogen and one chlorine atom.

Avogadro's hypothesis made possible the introduction of a system of atomic and molecular weights. If the weight of a hydrogen atom is arbitrarily set equal to unity (hydrogen was at that time, and still is, the lightest element known), the weight of a hydrogen molecule is 2, and the weight of a liter of hydrogen gas containing n molecules will be $2n$. Similarly, if the weight of an oxygen atom is denoted by x, the weight of a liter of oxygen gas at the same temperature and pressure, containing n molecules, will be $2nx$. Therefore, the ratio of the weight of a liter of oxygen to the weight of a liter of hydrogen is x. It was found by weighing equal volumes of the two gases at the same temperature and pressure that x is very close to 16. Similarly, from studies of the way in which other elements combine with each other and with hydrogen and oxygen in the gaseous state, it was possible to obtain the atomic and molecular weights of other gaseous elements and compounds. By about 1815, the atomic weights of all known elements had been obtained by various methods and with varying degrees of accuracy.

Following from this concept of the atomic weight of an element, and the molecular weight of a compound, was the *gram atomic weight* or *gram molecular weight* of an element or a compound. This is the amount of an element or compound whose weight in grams equals its atomic or molecular weight. By an application of Avogadro's hypothesis, the number of atoms in a gram atom of an element, or the number of molecules in a gram molecule, is the same in all cases. This number is now generally called *Avogadro's number*, and is denoted by N_0. Although its value was not known, it was believed to be large but finite.

In 1833, Michael Faraday was engaged in the study of the relation of electricity to chemistry. In particular, he was interested in the decomposition of substances which occurs when an electric current is passed through them. It had been known since the second half of the eighteenth century that an electrical discharge between two poles immersed in water is accompanied by the generation of hydrogen gas at one pole and of oxygen gas at the other. Later experiments showed that many aqueous solutions are decomposed into their constituents when electricity is passed through them. It was further shown that many solid compounds which are not ordinarily conductors of electricity become conductors when liquefied by fusion, and can be decomposed in the same way as aqueous solutions.

Faraday called this phenomenon of electrochemical decomposition *electrolysis*. The substance directly decomposed by the passage of the current he called the *electrolyte*, and the products of the decomposition, *ions*. The terminals, or poles, through which the electric current enters or leaves the electrolyte were named *electrodes*. Each of the two electrodes received its own special designation. The one at the higher potential, from which the current enters the electrolyte, he called the *anode*, and the products of decomposition, oxygen, for example, and acids in general, which collected there he called *anions*. The electrode at the lower potential, by which the current leaves the electrolyte, became known as the *cathode*, and the ions which collected there, hydrogen, for example, and metals and bases in general, he called *cations*.

Late in 1832, Faraday had suggested that the mass of any ion deposited at an electrode in a given time depends only on the total amount of electricity (the product of the current and the time) passing through it. It is independent of such factors as the size of the electrodes or the concentration of the solution. He verified this law experimentally in 1833, and it is now known as Faraday's First Law of Electrolysis. He then went on to compare the masses of the ions liberated when the same amount of electricity was passed through different electrolytes. He found that the mass of any ion deposited by the same amount of electricity is proportional to the ionic weight divided by its valency. For our purposes, the *valency* of an ion can be taken to be equal to the number of hydrogen atoms with which it can combine. For example, the chloride ion is monovalent as follows from the formula HCl for hydrogen chloride, while oxygen is divalent as it is known to combine with two atoms of hydrogen to form water, which has the formula H_2O. By ionic weight, we mean the sum of the atomic weights of the atoms making up the ion, taking the atomic weight of ordinary oxygen to be 16. This discovery of Faraday's is now called his Second Law of Electrolysis. It led him to suppose that the amount of electricity passing through the electrolyte is exactly equal to the amount of electricity possessed by the ions collected at each of the electrodes, that is, to the *total charge* on the ions at each electrode. The quantity of electricity required to accumulate one gram ion of any monovalent ion was found by Faraday to be equal to 800,000 times the amount obtainable from a battery of Leyden jars, charged by thirty turns of a very large and powerful electric machine in full action. In modern units, this quantity of electricity, called the *faraday*, is equal to 96,493 coulombs and is denoted by F.

It was believed for a long time that the molecules of an electrolyte were decomposed into ions by the action of the externally applied electric force, which then drove them toward the electrodes. However, since several consequences of this theory were contradicted by experiment, it had to be discarded.

A superior explanation of electrical conductivity in electrolytes was suggested by the German physicist R. Clausius in 1857. Following a suggestion made by Williamson seven years earlier, Clausius hypothesized that even in the absence of an external electric force, in a compound liquid such as water the constituent molecules are constantly decomposing into ions, some of which recombine with each other. For example, the aqueous solution of sodium chloride, ordinary table salt, already contains a certain number of positively charged sodium ions and an equal number of negatively charged chloride ions. The applied electric force merely exerts a force on these ions which causes them to drift preferentially toward the cathode and anode, respectively. The existence of positively and negatively charged ions strongly suggested that the forces which bind them into compounds, such as sodium chloride, are electrical in nature, and that when these compounds are introduced into water, the electrical forces holding the ions together are weakened, enabling them to separate and assume an independent existence.

From the fact that a gram ionic weight of any univalent ion contains Avogadro's number N_O of ions and from the value of the faraday, it would have been possible in principle for Faraday to determine the quantity of electricity associated with any univalent ion. This quantity, called the *ionic charge* and denoted by e, is given by $e = F/N_O$. Faraday did not calculate the value of the ionic charge because the value of Avogadro's number was not known at the time of his investigations. However, the results of Faraday's researches are no less valuable because of this omission, since they were the first to suggest the atomicity of electric charge, that is, that there exists a smallest or elementary charge.

In discussing the solutions of a particular problem, there are two general points of view we can adopt. We can prove that a solution to the problem exists, without specifying how it can be obtained. In some cases the knowledge of the existence of a solution, without knowing what it is, is sufficient to enable further progress to be made. Alternatively, we can prove the existence of a solution by actually constructing it and verifying that it has the required attributes. The former approach, which concerns itself with the establishment of existence theorems, is represented by Faraday's results, demonstrating the existence of an elementary electric charge. The latter approach can be termed "proof by construction." It characterizes the investigations carried on after the researches of Faraday described here, which culminated in the elucidation of the nature of this elementary charge, as well as its magnitude.

The early experiments which ultimately led to the establishment of the elementary charge were concerned with the passage of electricity through gases, but it must be emphasized that the great majority of these experiments were not carried out with this goal in mind. Most of the early experimenters were primarily interested in determining the mechanism whereby air and other gases conducted electricity and the way the conductivity varied with the gas and other parameters. It was only later, in interpreting the results of various experiments, that the investigators were led to the idea of an elementary charge and focused their attention on its properties.

Experiments on electrical effects in gases, both at atmospheric and at low pressures, had been conducted for many years. In 1705, Francis Hauksbee observed a luminosity when glass was rubbed in air at low pressures, and in the 1740's Grummert in Germany and William Watson in England were studying continuous discharges in evacuated tubes. In 1821, Sir Humphrey Davy, using a powerful battery, produced an arc in air between two carbon electrodes, which persisted as the electrodes were separated as much as four inches. Repeating the experiment with the electrodes in an evacuated vessel, he found that the arc once formed could be drawn out to a length of six or seven inches. More interestingly, the arc was deflected by a magnet brought up to it. Other investigators during this period studied the nature of the transmission of electricity through different gases at atmospheric pressure.

Faraday's attention was attracted to problems connected with the passage of electricity through gases at low pressures. In 1838, while conducting an experiment in which he passed a current between two brass terminals in a tube containing air at very low pressure, he noticed that a purple stream proceeded from the positive electrode toward the negative, but stopped short of the negative electrode,

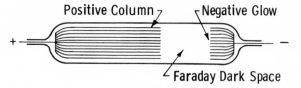

Figure 3.1

which was itself covered by a continuous glow. The narrow dark space separating the cathode from the purple glow is now called the *Faraday dark space* (see Fig. 3.1).

As the pressure in the tube is reduced, striking new effects occur. The cathode is still bathed in a thin layer of luminosity. However, next to this, as we proceed toward the anode, there is a dark space called the *Crookes dark space*. Its width depends on the pressure of the gas, increasing as the pressure is lowered, and may depend on the current passing through the tube. Past the Crookes dark space, there is a luminous region, the negative glow, which is followed by a second dark region, the Faraday dark space. Beyond the Faraday dark space, we again have the luminous positive column which extends right up to the anode. Under proper conditions of gas pressure and electric current, the positive column can consist of alternate light and dark regions called *striations*. These features of the discharge are shown schematically in Fig. 3.2 and also in the actual photograph.

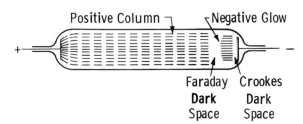

Figure 3.2

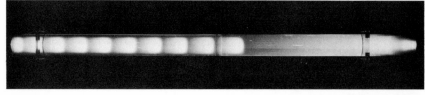

(Westinghouse Research Laboratory)

Photograph of Crookes tube, showing striations, the Faraday dark space, and the Crookes dark space.

Although physicists who followed Faraday carried out many investigations to determine just how the nature of the discharge in the tube was affected by the tube size and shape, the gas pressure, electric current, and the type of gas in the tube, further real progress in this field was held up for nearly twenty years by purely technical difficulties. The pressures in the tubes used in these investigations, while low, were still too high to permit effective study of the phenomena discovered by Faraday. However, in 1855 the German physicist Heinrich Geissler invented the mercury vapor pump and it became possible to pursue investigations at pressures far below those previously attainable.

The first results obtained with the new tubes made possible by Geissler's invention were those of the German physicist Julius Plücker, in the years 1858 and 1859. In his earliest experiments, he showed that the negative glow was deflected by a magnet. When he reduced the cathode to a point and brought a magnet up to the negative glow, he found that the bright boundary of the negative glow coincided with the lines of magnetic force passing through the point cathode. He likened this behavior to that of a collection of iron filings having perfect freedom of motion in the same magnetic field. However, his most interesting result was obtained when the pressure in his tube was decreased to the point where the Crookes dark space filled the entire tube. When this occurs, the walls of the tube begin to fluoresce. Plücker noticed during one of his experiments that this fluorescence was not uniform over his tube, but occurred in bright greenish-yellow patches on the tube's surface near the cathode. He further noted that the positions of these bright patches moved when a magnet was brought up to the tube. He ascribed the patchy glow to electric currents which proceeded from the cathode to the walls of the tube and then, for some reason, returned to the cathode along the same path. This discovery of Plücker's, in 1859, was the first direct clue which would lead to the discovery of the electron.

The next advance came in 1869, when a former pupil of Plücker's, W. Hittorf, discovered that a solid object placed between a pointed cathode and the wall of a highly evacuated tube cast a well-defined shadow of itself on the tube's wall. This effect was independent of whether the solid was opaque or transparent, a conductor or an insulator. In 1876, Eugen Goldstein repeated this experiment using a cathode of finite size, much larger than the solid object which was placed close to the cathode. The small object still cast a well-defined shadow on the wall of the tube opposite the cathode. This was an important result since, taken together with Hittorf's observation, it showed that the invisible rays producing the fluorescence on the walls of the tube emanate in a definite direction from each point of the cathode. Goldstein found that this direction is perpendicular to the surface of the cathode at that point. In this respect, the emission of these rays from the cathode differs from that of light from an incandescent surface. For if an object which is small compared with a flat light source is brought close to the source, it will not cast an appreciable shadow, because of the fact that the light is emitted in all directions from each point of the source.

The nature of these "cathode rays" provoked a great deal of speculation. Goldstein himself believed them to be waves which propagated through an all-pervading medium called "the ether." This was to the cathode rays as water to ocean waves. In this he was influenced by the current belief that light was of this nature. However, even before Goldstein's experiments, the English physicist Cromwell Varley had suggested in 1871 that the rays are negatively charged particles ejected from the cathode by the electric current flowing out of it. These particles were assumed to be of the dimensions of ordinary gaseous molecules.

In 1879, Sir William Crookes, for whom the Crookes dark space is named, published the results of a series of experiments which had the effect of largely confirming Varley's suggestions concerning the nature of the cathode rays. In one of his earliest experiments, he confirmed the fact that the cathode rays are emitted normally to the surface of the cathode. He did this by placing the cathode along the axis of the tube and the anode off the tube's axis, about halfway along its length. An object placed in the tube on the far side of the anode from the cathode still cast a shadow on the wall of the tube opposite the cathode. This result indicated that the success of the experiment did not depend on the position of the anode. The cathode rays do not travel from the cathode to the anode, but emanate in straight lines from the cathode.

Crookes next performed an experiment whose results he interpreted as showing that two streams of cathode rays repelled each other and therefore were composed of particles carrying electric charges. It is now known that although his experimental results in this case were correct, his interpretation of them was not entirely accurate. Nevertheless, proceeding on the basis of his erroneous conclusions, Crookes was led to other correct and important results. He determined the sign of the charge on the charged particles comprising the cathode rays. A tube was constructed with a slit in front of the cathode to confine the rays to a ribbon. This ribbon of rays intercepted a chalked screen, slightly inclined to the axis of the tube, and this fluoresced when struck by the rays, displaying their path. A horseshoe magnet, placed over the tube as in Fig. 3.3, deflected the rays downward. When the poles of the magnet were reversed, the rays were deflected upward.

To interpret these results Crookes used a result discovered by Faraday in 1821. Faraday had found experimentally that a force is exerted by a magnetic field on a current-carrying conductor (the magnetic lines of force assumed directed from the north pole to the south pole). The force is perpendicular to the direction of the magnetic field and to the direction of the current flow, being directed along the line of advance of a right-handed screw as the direction of the current is rotated into the direction of the field. It should be remarked that Faraday's rule was originally derived for material conductors such as wires; however, in 1838, he asserted that if a ball were positively charged with electricity and then moved in any direction, effects would be produced as if an electric current in this same direction had existed. This was confirmed experimentally by Rowland in 1876.

From the direction of deflection of the cathode rays, with the experimental arrangement shown in Fig. 3.3, Crookes deduced from Faraday's rule that the direction of the current flow was from right to

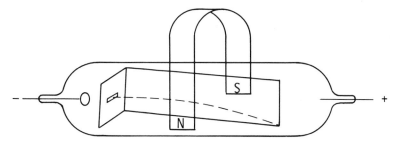

Figure 3.3

left in this figure, that is, from the anode to the cathode. At the time of Crookes' researches, it was commonly accepted that the current flowing from the anode to the cathode in a conductor consisted of a flow of positive electricity from the cathode to the anode. Now, the experiments of Hittorf and Goldstein, and the earlier work of Crookes himself, had shown conclusively that the cathode rays emanated from the cathode. Crookes accordingly identified them with the flow of negative electricity from the cathode to the anode. He assumed cathode rays to be negatively charged atoms, the *ions* of the chemists, which had obtained their charge by colliding with the cathode. He argued that the main difference between conduction in electrolytes and in evacuated tubes lay in the average distance an ion could travel in each case before colliding with another. In the case of a relatively dense medium, such as a liquid, any given ion can travel only a short distance before colliding with another. Because of the random nature of the collisions, the path traced by an ion in going from one electrode to another will be highly irregular. In a gas at a very low pressure the probability of a collision between two ions is very small and, as a result, an ion can travel in a straight line for an appreciable distance.

The idea that electricity possesses a discrete rather than a wavelike or continuous nature received support from the noted German physicist H. von Helmholtz. In 1881, Helmholtz commented, "If we accept the hypothesis that the elementary substances are composed of atoms, we cannot avoid concluding that electricity also, positive as well as negative, is divided into definite elementary portions which behave like atoms of electricity."

In the following year, the German physicist W. Giese applied to the phenomena in discharge tubes the ideas which had been developed many years earlier to explain the conductivity of aqueous solutions. He suggested that small numbers of gaseous ions are present in a gas at ordinary temperatures and pressures, their numbers increasing with increasing temperatures. These ions, which are charged atoms or molecules, move under the influence of the electric field set up by the electrodes, and thus carry current. This idea was taken up by Schuster in England two years later. On the basis of certain experimental observations, he concluded that molecules striking a charged surface, such as the cathode of a discharge tube, could not carry away any of the charge. This meant that the origin of the cathode rays could not be exactly that proposed by Crookes. Like Giese, Schuster felt that dissociation of the gas molecules in a discharge tube was a necessary prelude to the passage of a current through the tube.

Other objections were quickly raised to Crookes' suggestion about the nature of the cathode rays. If, as it was believed at the time, the flow of current from the anode to the cathode was the superposition of oppositely directed streams of positive and negative electricity, then where was the accompanying stream of positive electricity flowing from the anode to the cathode? This question was answered by Goldstein in 1886. Reasoning that the presence of the cathode rays in the region between the cathode and anode might interfere with the observation of the positive rays in this region, he bored holes in the cathode and set it opposite to the anode. He then discovered that something was passing through these holes in the direction assumed for the positive flow. A glow appeared behind each of the holes which disappeared if an obstruction were in front of the hole. The rays responsible for the glow Goldstein called *canal rays*. These rays were visible, unlike the cathode rays which are invisible unless they impinge on a fluorescing material. The color of the flow depended on the particular gas in the tube, while all the observed properties of the cathode rays were independent of this gas. Furthermore, their deflection by a magnetic field was in the direction opposite to the deflection of the cathode rays by the same field. The evidence was thus fairly convincing that the canal rays constituted the positive flow of electricity assumed to accompany the negative flow.

Although one objection to Crookes' hypothesis about the nature of the cathode rays had been disposed of, others were soon raised. In 1883, Heinrich Hertz argued that if the cathode rays were a stream of charged atoms they should be deflected by an electric field. When he failed to observe this effect experimentally, he rejected the hypothesis of Varley and Crookes regarding the nature of the cathode rays.

Then in 1892, Hertz performed an experiment in which a thin window, or film, of gold or aluminum was placed perpendicular to the axis of a discharge tube, completely separating the cathode from that part of the tube on the far side of the window. It was found that the walls of the tube on the far side from the cathode still fluoresced, showing that at least some of the cathode rays had penetrated the film. Since the film was thick enough to be opaque to light, and certainly too thick to permit the passage of even the smallest gaseous atoms, Hertz's result indicated that if the cathode rays were indeed electrified particles of some kind, their size had to be smaller than that of the atoms in the film. Otherwise they could not pass readily through the spaces between these atoms.

Similar results were obtained by Hertz's pupil, Phillip Lenard, who mounted the metal window in the wall of the tube, opposite the cathode. He found that the cathode rays passed through this window and caused the air to fluoresce for an inch beyond it.

It was about this time, in 1894, that the English physicist G. Johnston Stoney gave the name "electron" to the charged particles which were believed, at least by the British physicists, to comprise the cathode rays. However, the controversy about their nature still continued, with the majority of the German physicists adhering to the view that they were waves in the ether.

In 1894, J. J. Thomson succeeded in measuring the speed of the cathode rays by means of a rotating mirror and found it to be about a thousandth of the speed of light. This result made it hard to believe that the cathode rays were waves in the ether, since the ether had been introduced into physics specifically as a medium which would propagate waves with a speed equal to that of light and no other. A year later the French physicist Jean Perrin constructed a discharge tube in which a collector tube, connected to an electroscope, was mounted on the axis of the tube opposite the cathode. The collector was shielded and the shielding, which formed the anode, was grounded so that the assumed negatively charged particles would not be preferentially attracted to the collector by the presence of a positive potential on it. It was found that the electroscope became negatively charged when the cathode rays were produced. It was difficult to understand how waves propagating in the ether could accumulate in the collector, but the results were readily understandable if the rays consisted of charged particles.

Perrin's experiment was repeated by J. J. Thomson in a slightly modified form to disprove the argument offered by some that Perrin's results did not demonstrate that the electric charges which accompanied the cathode rays were bound to them. Thomson's modification consisted of focusing the cathode rays by passing them through a hole

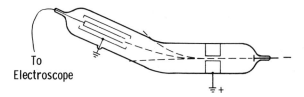

To
Electroscope

Figure 3.4

in a grounded anode, and removing the grounded collector to one side of the rays' path. (This is shown schematically in Fig. 3.4.) When the tube was in operation, the electroscope indicated that only a very small amount of charge was accumulating in the collector. However, when the beam of cathode rays was deflected by a magnet in such a way that it entered the collector, the electroscope immediately showed a large deflection, indicating an accumulation of negative charge in the collector. When the beam was even further deflected, so that again it missed the opening to the collector, the charge on the electroscope fell almost to zero. Thomson concluded from these results that the flow of negative electricity in the tube followed the path of the cathode rays.

During the course of this experiment, Thomson noticed that when the cathode rays were deflected into the collector, the charge on the electroscope did not increase indefinitely but eventually reached a value above which it would not increase. He interpreted this result as being caused by the gas in the tube becoming conductive because of the cathode rays passing through it. Thus some of the negative charge acquired by the cathode would be conducted away through the gas to the anode, and the steady state found by Thomson occurred when the rate at which the collector lost charge by this mechanism equalled the rate at which it acquired charge from the cathode rays. He confirmed this interpretation with two experiments. In the first, he gave the collector an initial negative charge which was less than the steady state charge he had found previously. In the second experiment, the initial negative charge was greater than the steady state charge. In the former case, the charge on the electroscope increased under the influence of the cathode rays, while in the latter case, a portion of the initial charge was conducted away through the gas, due to the conductivity it acquired by the passage of the cathode rays.

These experiments illustrate well that quality possessed by Thomson to a rare degree, the ability to devise an experiment so that its results illuminate in an unambiguous way the point being studied. He is generally regarded as the foremost experimental physicist of his day, a view which, while justified, tends to relegate to second rank his important contributions to theoretical physics.

The experiments of Perrin and Thomson virtually killed the theory of cathode rays as waves in an ether. However, before the competing particle theory could gain whole-hearted acceptance, the results of Hertz and Lenard had to be explained. This task was undertaken by J. J. Thomson. Lenard's result, that the cathode rays could travel unhindered as much as an inch in air at atmospheric pressure, indicated to Thomson that they could not be charged atoms or molecules, as Crookes had supposed. The mean free path of an air molecule at atmospheric pressure had been determined by that time to be of the order of one-hundred-thousandth of an inch. Even if the molecule were injected into air at high speed, it would undergo so many collisions with the air molecules in traveling through the gas that its speed would be reduced to half its initial value in a distance of a few multiples of its mean free path, a distance much smaller than an inch. "Thus," he said, "from Lenard's experiments on the absorption of the rays outside the tube, it follows on the hypothesis that the cathode rays are charged particles moving with high velocities that the size of the carriers must be small compared with the dimensions of ordinary atoms or molecules. We see on this hypothesis why the magnetic deflection is the same inside the tube whatever be the nature of the gas, for the carriers are the same whatever gas be used." This conclusion is in agreement with the observed passage of the cathode rays through the metal windows, as we have remarked previously. Then with a statement reminiscent of Helmholtz's sixteen years earlier, Thomson continued, "The assumption of a state of matter more finely subdivided than the atom of an element is a somewhat startling one; but a hypothesis that would involve somewhat similar consequences—viz. that the so-called elements are compounds of some primordial element—has been put forward from time to time by various chemists."*

---

* *A History of the Theories of Aether and Electricity by Sir Edmund Whittaker, published by Thomas Nelson and Sons, Ltd., London; American edition published by Harper and Row, New York and Evanston.*

Thomson now turned his attention to Hertz's failure to achieve the deflection of the cathode rays by an electric field. On the basis of the results of his repetition of Perrin's experiment, he conjectured that the passage of cathode rays through the gas in the tube had the effect of ionizing it; the gas molecules were broken up into positively and negatively charged parts. Therefore, in Hertz's experiment, where the cathode rays were passed between two parallel plates, one charged positively and the other negatively, he supposed that the positive gas ions were attracted to the negative plate and the negative ions to the positive plate, annulling the electric field between them. To avoid this happening in his experiments, Thomson reduced the pressure of the gas in his tube far below that previously used in such experiments. This decreased the number of gas molecules in the tube and consequently the number of ions that could be produced. At sufficiently low pressures, he found that the cathode rays were indeed deflected by an electric field. With this result, resistance to the corpuscular theory of cathode rays ended. Interest now centered on determining the properties, such as the charge and mass, of the electrons comprising the cathode rays.

In his first attempt at such a determination, Thomson mounted a thermocouple in the path of the cathode rays, enclosing it in a collector tube of the type used in Perrin's experiment and in his modification of it. Assuming that all electrons entering the collector struck the thermocouple and gave up their kinetic energy to it in the form of heat, from the increase of temperature indicated by the thermocouple and the physical properties of the thermocouple, Thomson was able to determine W, the heat given up by electrons. Since this equals the kinetic energy of the electrons, he had the relation $W = \frac{1}{2} nmv^2$, where n is the number of electrons entering the collector, m is their mass, and v their speed. If each electron carries a charge e, the total charge Q registered by the electroscope is equal to ne, thus $Q = ne$. The electrons were now deflected into a circular path by the application of an external magnetic field, whose strength we denote by H. As we will see in the next chapter, the radius R of the circular path followed by the electrons is given by $R = mv/eH$. We therefore have three relations involving the four unknowns, n, m, e, v. Since we are not interested in finding n, we eliminate it between the first two relations and use the resulting two expressions,

$$\frac{2W}{Q} = \frac{m}{e} v^2,$$

$$HR = \frac{m}{e} v,$$

to obtain the electron's speed v and the ratio e/m. It is easily found that

$$v = \frac{2W}{QHR}, \qquad \frac{e}{m} = \frac{2W}{QH^2R^2}.$$

From the experimentally determined values of W, Q, and R, and the known value of H, Thomson obtained values for v of the same order of magnitude as those obtained by the rotating mirror method three years earlier. The really surprising result of his measurements was the very large value he found for e/m, about 1000 times larger than the value found for a hydrogen ion from the electrolysis of water.

Before publishing his results, however, Thomson verified them by a different method. We have pointed out previously that a charged particle is deflected by an electric field as well as by a magnetic field. The force on a particle carrying a charge e, exerted by an electric field whose strength is E, is $F_e = Ee$. The magnitude of the force exerted on the same particle by a magnetic field of strength H is given by Heaviside's expression $F_m = Hev$. If the electric and magnetic fields are directed at right angles to each other, these two forces will act on the particle in opposite directions. By adjusting the relative strengths of the electric and magnetic fields so that the beam of cathode rays passing through his tube suffered no deflection, Thomson determined the velocity of the electrons from the relation $v = E/H$, which follows from the condition $F_e = F_m$. He then switched off the electric field and measured the deflection of the spot made by the cathode rays on a fluorescent screen opposite the cathode. From this, and the dimensions of the tube, he could calculate the radius of curvature of the cathode ray beam, which as we mentioned earlier is given by $R = mv/eH$. Since v had just been determined in an independent experiment, the value of the ratio e/m followed directly from this relation. His new results confirmed his earlier ones that the ratio e/m for electrons is about 1000 times that for a hydrogen ion. Thomson also showed that this value of the e/m ratio was independent of the nature of the gas in the tube, the metal out of which the electrodes were made, and the glass out of which the tube was constructed. More accurate measurements made by many workers since 1897 show that this ratio is very close to 1837 times that for the hydrogen ion.

The result that the cathode ray particles, or electrons, were the same whatever the gas in the discharge tube, together with his belief that particles smaller than atoms could exist, led Thomson to suppose first that the electrons were the ultimate building blocks of which atoms are formed. They can be torn out of the atom by the potential difference between anode and cathode, by heating the atom in an arc, and Thomson had just shown that gases irradiated with the recently discovered x rays also became conducting, that is, ionized. However, eventually Thomson had to modify his ideas regarding the composition of atoms. Since the electrons possess a negative charge, while an atom is electrically neutral, some portion of the atom must consist of positive charge, whose amount balances the negative charge of the electrons. Originally Thomson had believed that the very large values of e/m, relative to the hydrogen ion, he had found for the electrons was due both to a large value of e and a small value of m. However, the last argument convinced him that this could not be the case. For, if an ion is formed by the tearing away of electrons from an atom, the charge on the electron cannot be greater than that of the ion of the atom from which it was removed. Thus, the charge on an electron cannot be larger than that of a hydrogen ion, so that the large value of e/m for an electron, compared to that for a hydrogen ion, cannot be due to any disparity in the charges. Rather it implies that the mass of the electron is about $1/1837$ that of the hydrogen ion, if the ion is formed by the removal of only a single electron from the atom. Should the ion be formed by the removal of two electrons, the mass of the electron would be $1/3674$ that of the hydrogen ion. It is clear that a determination of the charge or mass of the electron would also yield valuable information about the nature of ionized atoms.

These ideas of Thomson's also answered a question which had been puzzling physicists for many years: how could an elemental gas, such as hydrogen or helium, become ionized? We have referred previously to the suggestions of Giese and Schuster regarding the nature of electrical conductivity in gases. They suggested that the current was carried by electrified atoms or ions, but the nature of these ions was not understood at that time. The ionization of compounds, such as sodium chloride, in aqueous solutions was understood to represent the separation of a molecule into positively and negatively charged portions, one associated with the sodium atom, the other with the chloride atom. However, helium gas was known to be monatomic, that is, a molecule of helium consists of a single atom. Yet it, too, could be rendered conductive by the passage of cathode rays through it, and this implied that individual neutral atoms could be separated into positively and negatively charged parts. Thomson identified the negatively charged part with electrons removed from the helium atoms, and the positively charged part with the positively charged atomic residue left behind.

It now remained only to determine the values of e and m separately. Actually, only one of these quantities had to be determined, since the remaining one could then be obtained from the known value of the e/m ratio.

The method which yielded the charge on an electron had its origin in the observation made by the French chemist Coulier in 1875, that if ordinary air is compressed in a vessel containing water, a cloud is formed when the air becomes saturated with water vapor and is allowed to expand quickly. Coulier found that the formation of the cloud depended on the presence of dust particles in the air, since if the air were filtered before being admitted to the expansion chamber, no cloud was formed when the expansion took place. The dust particles provided centers at which the water vapor could condense into droplets. He also found that clouds could be formed in filtered air if a platinum wire was heated to a high temperature in the air, or if a small hydrogen flame burned in the air for a short time before the expansion. The great British physicist Lord Kelvin showed theoretically that in order for particles to act as nuclei for condensation, they had to be larger than a certain critical size, which was large compared to atomic dimensions. Soon after this, J. J. Thomson showed that a particle much smaller than the critical size determined by Lord Kelvin could still act as an effective condensation center, provided it carried an electric charge. This prediction of Thomson's was verified experimentally by C. T. R. Wilson in 1897. Wilson ionized a filtered gas by exposing it to x rays or ultraviolet radiation, and showed that a cloud was produced by expansions too small to produce them in an un-ionized gas. He also found that by controlling the degree of expansion, he could cause condensation to take place about negative ions, but not about positive ions.

Thomson proceeded from his belief that the ionization of a gas, for example, by the action of x rays, consists of the removal of electrons from the gas atoms, leaving behind positively charged ions. In an expansion chamber of the type used by Wilson in his experiments, in which condensation occurred only about negative drops, the number of cloud drops would equal the number of electrons in the chamber. Knowing the number of drops present and the total charge carried by them, the charge per electron follows directly. To determine the number of drops in the expansion chamber, Thomson used a result obtained almost fifty years earlier by Sir George Stokes. In a theoretical calculation of the greatest velocity which falling raindrops can achieve, he found that it depended on the size of the drops, their density relative to that of air, and the viscosity of the air. From the rate at which a fog droplet fell, Thomson could infer its size. By thermodynamic arguments, being able to calculate the amount of water vapor condensed into fog, he was also able to calculate the number of drops and hence the number of electrons in the chamber. He then applied a potential difference of a volt across the chamber and measured the current which flowed through the gas. The current is proportional to the total charge on the cloud and to the average velocity of the drops in the potential difference. The latter could be obtained from an independent measurement. Division by the number of electrons present gave him the charge per electron. The value found by Thomson was of the order of 3×10^{-10} electrostatic units of charge per electron. Combining this result with his previous value for e/m, he obtained a value of 10^{-27} grams for the mass of the electron. Assuming that the hydrogen ion was formed by the removal of a single electron from a hydrogen atom, the mass of a hydrogen atom would then be approximately 2000 times larger than this, or 10^{-24} grams. Then, since one gram atomic weight of hydrogen contains Avogadro's number, N_0, of atoms, we find that N_0 is of the order of 10^{24}.

These numbers are respectively so small and so large that no pictorial representation can make them comprehensible. Does it mean anything to say that the number of atoms in a gram atom of an element is so large that if we were to write down on a strip of paper a one for every atom, writing ten figures on every inch of the strip, the length of the strip would equal 40,000 trips to the star nearest our sun, which is four light-years away? Yet the fact that this number is so large and that the mass of the electron is so small is not what should surprise us. As T. W. Chalmers has put it, what should surprise us is that the discovery of the magnitudes of the scale on which nature operates should have been within the power of man.

Thomson's determination of the charge on the electron was subject to at least two uncertainties. First, there existed the possibility that a fog droplet, which had condensed about an electron or a negatively charged particle, might have acquired a second charge, with the result that the number of drops would not equal the number of electrons in the expansion chamber. Second, the water drops might evaporate, losing mass, which would also lead to an error in the determination of the number of electrons. To avoid errors arising from these sources, the American physicist Robert A. Millikan devised an ingenious method for the determination of the electronic charge.

Millikan's experimental setup is shown schematically in Fig. 3.5. Rather than work with the whole fog of droplets condensed onto negative ions or electrons, he focused his attention on individual droplets. To avoid errors arising from the evaporation of the drops, he used nonvolatile liquids such as oil or mercury. Drops of these liquids were produced by an atomizer, and in the course of their formation they became charged by friction. Some of them would drift down through a very small opening in the upper plate into the space between a pair of electrified plates. This space was illuminated by an electric arc outside the apparatus, and a microscope eyepiece containing two horizontal hairlines a measured distance apart was trained on this space. Seen through the eyepiece, an oil drop showed up like a star against

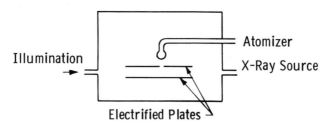

Figure 3.5

a dark background. The entire apparatus was immersed in a constant temperature bath. From the time required for an oil drop to fall the distance between the hairlines, with no potential difference across the plates, Millikan could determine its dimensions, and hence its mass, from Stokes' relation. If now the plates were charged so that a uniform electric field was produced between them, a force was exerted on the oil drop in a vertical direction. Either he could adjust the strength of the field so that the electric force just balanced the gravitational force acting on the oil drop, or he could set the field strength arbitrarily and measure the new velocity of the drop. In either case, knowing the magnitude of the electric force acting on the oil drops to be $F_e = Ee$, where e is the charge on the drop, and knowing from the drop's mass the gravitational force acting on it, he was able to determine directly the value of the charge on the drop. Proceeding in this way, Millikan found from the results of many experiments that although the charge on an oil drop could vary from drop to drop, it was always an integral multiple of a certain smallest charge, which he determined to be 4.774×10^{-10} electrostatic units. This he assumed was the charge on the electron, a supposition which has withstood the test of time. Ten years later it was discovered that the value for the viscosity of air Millikan used in his calculations was too low by about 0.5 percent. Using the corrected value of the viscosity, the value of e obtained is 4.804×10^{-10} electrostatic units.

Millikan's results are important for two reasons: Not only did they provide an accurate value for the electronic charge, but he had shown conclusively the atomicity of charge.

Thomson's discovery that electrons are one of the building blocks of atoms had consequences for atomic and nuclear physics, as well as for other branches of physics, whose effects are still felt today. There is no branch of science, from chemistry to the structure of solids, from astrophysics to the study of the nature of the elementary particles comprising the atomic nucleus, in which Thomson's discoveries have not played a part.

Action and Reaction

4

Taming
the Free Electron

IT IS OBVIOUS that in order to utilize electron motion for practical purposes, we must first know how the electron behaves when subjected to a force. What is the motion of an electron in an electric field, for example, and how can this motion be controlled? To answer these questions, we must understand the force between charged bodies, and this requires a quantitative expression with which we can work. We mentioned earlier an amount of charge called a coulomb. This was named for the French physicist Charles Augustin Coulomb, who in 1785 showed experimentally that the force F between two charged bodies could be written

$$F = \frac{q_1 q_2}{r^2_{1,2}}, \qquad (4.1)$$

where q_1 and q_2 are the charges on the two bodies (which can be either positive or negative) and $r_{1,2}$ is the distance between them. It is often convenient to think of the charge q_1 as exerting a force F on charge q_2, and thus we might write

$$F = \left[\frac{q_1}{r^2_{1,2}} \right] q_2. \qquad (4.2)$$

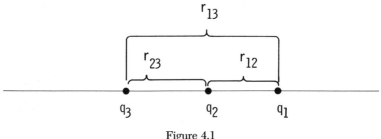

Figure 4.1

In this form, we can see that the force on q_2 is proportional to the magnitude of the charge q_2, the proportionality factor depending on q_1 and on the distance $r_{1,2}$. If we now have three charges, as shown in Fig. 4.1, we can write the force between them:

$$F_{1,2} = \frac{q_1 q_2}{r^2_{1,2}}$$

$$F_{1,3} = \frac{q_1 q_3}{r^2_{1,3}}$$

$$F_{2,3} = \frac{q_2 q_3}{r^2_{2,3}}.$$

In this case, what is the total force exerted on charge 1? We find that it is

$$F = \frac{q_1 q^2}{r^2_{1,2}} + \frac{q_3 q_1}{r^2_{1,3}} = \left[\frac{q_2}{r^2_{1,2}} + \frac{q_3}{r^2_{1,3}} \right] q_1. \qquad (4.3)$$

We see that the force on q_1 is again proportional to the magnitude of the charge q_1, the proportionality factor depending on the magnitude and position of the other charges. This holds true regardless of the number of charges involved, but when we are dealing with a large number, it is frequently easier to introduce the idea of an electric field.

The electric field E acting on a particle is defined as the ratio of the force acting on the particle in question to the charge of that particle. Thus,

$$E = \frac{F}{q_1}. \qquad (4.4)$$

The direction of the field is defined as the direction in which a positive charge would move. In the example of three particles given above, the electric field at q_1 is the parenthetical expression in Eq. 4.3. Often it is simpler just to specify the electric field at the position of q_1, instead of describing the position and charge of each particle acting on charge q_1. Then, using Newton's second law of motion ($F = ma$, where a is the acceleration and m the mass) we are able to describe completely the motion of a charged particle in an electric field. For example, let's suppose that we have a particle, initially at rest at a point $x = 0$ in a constant electric field of magnitude E, acting in the direction of the positive x axis. From Newton's law, we have

$$a = \frac{F}{m} = \frac{qE}{m}. \tag{4.5}$$

Since E is constant, the acceleration is also constant. Now, as we mentioned earlier, the acceleration is the time rate of change of the velocity, or simply the change in velocity in a given length of time. This means that

$$a = \frac{v(t) - v_0}{t - t_0}. \tag{4.6}$$

Here $v(t)$ is the velocity at a time t, and v_0 is the velocity at a time t_0. Since we have said that the particle in our example was initially at rest at $x = 0$, we may take $v_0 = 0$ at $t_0 = 0$. We then have

$$\frac{v}{t} = a = \frac{qE}{m},$$

or

$$v = \frac{qE}{m} t. \tag{4.7}$$

This expression gives us the velocity at any time t. Now, to find the distance traveled in a given time, we must be a little careful. After a certain length of time, the average velocity is

$$\bar{v} = \frac{v_0 + v(t)}{2} = \frac{qE}{m} \frac{t}{2}. \tag{4.8}$$

After t seconds, then, the distance traveled is

$$x = \bar{v}t = \frac{qE}{m} \frac{t^2}{2}. \tag{4.9}$$

Using these rather simple ideas, we have succeeded in expressing the complicated motion of a charged particle in an electric field.

Now let's use this background to introduce the concept of potential energy and electric potential.

We have seen that the motion of a charged particle is governed by Newton's second law of motion—$F = ma$, where the force is equal to qE. Starting with $F = ma$, we multiply both sides of the equation by $\bar{v}\Delta t$, the average velocity over a given interval of time multiplied by the time interval considered. Thus,

$$F\bar{v}\Delta t = ma\bar{v}\Delta t. \qquad (4.10)$$

Since $\bar{v}\Delta t$ is the distance traveled by the particle, the left side of the equation is simply the force exerted on the particle multiplied by the distance it moves. By definition, the product of force and distance is the work W done on the particle.

We now introduce the term potential energy, denoted by V. The *change* in potential energy, ΔV, is the *negative* of the work done on the particle by the force F. Notice that since we can talk only about changes in potential energy, this means we can choose any convenient reference level for the zero of potential energy.

Let's now examine the right-hand side of Eq. 4.10. Since

$$a = \frac{v - v_0}{t - t_0} \text{ and } \bar{v} = \frac{v + v_0}{2},$$

we have $\quad ma\bar{v}\Delta t = m\frac{v - v_0}{\Delta t} \times \frac{v + v_0}{2}\Delta t = \frac{m}{2}(v^2 - v_0^2).$

This is the change in the kinetic energy of the particle. Therefore, we can write Eq. 4.10 as

$$W = \frac{m}{2}(v^2 - v_0^2), \qquad (4.11)$$

which means that the work done by the force F goes into increasing the kinetic energy of the particle. Remembering that the change in potential energy V is equal to the negative of the work done by the force F, if we now introduce potential energy, we have

$$V + \frac{m}{2}(v^2 - v_0^2) = 0. \qquad (4.12)$$

Thus the sum of the changes in potential and kinetic energy is zero, and this means that any change in potential energy must be accompanied by an equal and opposite change in kinetic energy.

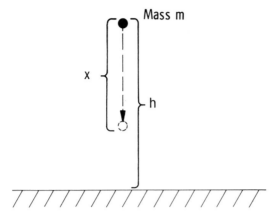

Figure 4.2

Although in deriving this we have had electrons and electric fields in mind, the result is quite general and valid for many types of forces. It may be helpful to illustrate these principles with the more familiar force of gravity. Referring to Fig. 4.2, let's suppose that a stone of mass m is dropped from a height h. Since the force exerted on the stone by gravity is mg, where g is the acceleration due to gravity, the gravitational force does an amount of work $(mg)(h)$ on the particle. This means that the *change* in potential energy is $-mgh$. From Eq. 4.12, we know that this loss of potential energy must show up as a gain in kinetic energy. In fact, since $v_0 = 0$, we have

$$v = (2gh)^{1/2}. \tag{4.13}$$

When the stone hits the ground, its velocity will be $(2gh)^{1/2}$.

Now let's consider the inverse problem. Suppose we shoot a stone vertically into the air with a speed v_0. We know that the force of gravity is acting in a downward direction, that is, the gravitational force tends to reduce the velocity, and the stone loses kinetic energy and gains potential energy. When the stone reaches a height x from the ground, the gravitational force has done an amount of work equal to $-mgx$. (Remember, the force is in the direction opposite to the motion, and therefore the work is negative.) Thus, the change in potential energy is $\Delta V = mgx$. From Eq. 4.12, we see that when the stone reaches a height $v_0^2/2g$, its velocity is zero. Therefore, it has converted all of its kinetic energy into potential energy.

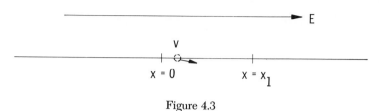

Figure 4.3

How do these ideas apply to the problem of a particle in an electric field? If the particle moves from $x = 0$ to $x = x_1$, as shown in Fig. 4.3, the work done by the field is qEx_1. Thus, the change in potential energy is equal to $-qEx_1$. For Eq. 4.12 to remain valid, the kinetic energy must increase. If the charge starts with a velocity to the left, the electric field will retard the particle, converting part of its kinetic energy into potential energy.

So far, we have considered the change or difference in potential energy. In dealing with electrons, it is convenient to define a new term, *potential,* which is simply the potential energy divided by the charge; in other words, it is the potential energy per unit charge. The usual unit of potential for charged particles is the *volt,* and the unit of potential energy is the *electron volt.* In the following chapters, we will frequently use the concept of potential, and it is important to realize that a high potential at a given point in space implies only a high potential energy for a *positive* charge. The negative charge has a correspondingly low potential energy at the same point, since as we have seen the potential is dependent on the sign of the charge.

MAGNETIC FORCES ON MOVING CHARGES

The motion of a charged particle in a magnetic field is a little more complicated than in an electric field. Before we can discuss this motion properly, we first need to review several ideas which may or may not be familiar.

Speaking generally, there are two different kinds of physical quantities in nature—*scalars* and *vectors.* A scalar is a quantity that is completely determined by a number. For example, the temperature of a body is completely determined by the number of degrees, Fahrenheit or Kelvin. Volume and density are other scalars. There are quantities, however, that can not be completely specified by a number; velocity, for example. When we say a car is traveling fifty miles an hour, we are obviously not defining the motion of the car completely, because we have not specified the direction in which it is moving. Quantities that require specifying both a magnitude (50 mph) and a direction (east) are called vectors.

We have already encountered several vectors in this chapter, although we did not point them out at the time. The electric field, for example, is a vector, since we needed to specify both the magnitude and the direction. Acceleration is also a vector, and it is easy to see that force is, too. Suppose we have a block of wood on a table, as shown in Fig. 4.4. Depending on the direction in which force is applied, the block may move to the left, the right, or not at all. Thus, to define a force we must give both its magnitude and its direction of application.

The reason that it is so important to understand these two terms is that handling scalar quantities is quite different from dealing with vector quantities. Let's first consider a scalar. Suppose to a block of wood of volume v we add a second block of equal volume. Obviously, the total volume of the two blocks is $2V$. The addition of scalar quantities is precisely the same as ordinary addition. But let's look at vector quantities. Suppose an airplane, in the absence of wind, travels east at a velocity v_0. Suddenly a wind springs up, blowing east at a velocity v_1. With this tailwind, the plane will now have a velocity of $v_0 + v_1$ toward the east. However, if the wind happened to be blowing west, it is easy to see that the plane's velocity eastward would be $v_0 - v_1$, provided the wind velocity does not exceed the plane's velocity in the absence of wind.

Now let's consider a more complicated situation. What happens if the wind is blowing south? One qualitative observation is immediately apparent. The net velocity of the plane will no longer be directed

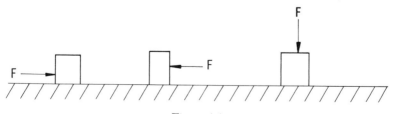

Figure 4.4

east, but rather south of east. But how can we find the quantitative answer? Let's consider what happens in an hour's time. During one hour, the plane is heading east with a velocity whose magnitude is v_0, but at the same time the wind is acting in a southerly direction with a velocity whose magnitude is v_1. After one hour, the plane will arrive at a certain point. Clearly, the magnitude of the velocity is the distance traveled (we consider this to be one hour), and the direction of the velocity is given by the direction of the end point from the starting point. The problem is to determine this end point, and to solve it, let's suppose first that the plane flies for one hour at its velocity v_0 *in the absence of wind.* At the end of one hour, the airplane's engines stop (yes, we know the plane will crash, but this is only a thought experiment) and then for an hour the wind blows at a velocity v. To determine the end point, we draw a vector v_0, as shown in Fig. 4.5a, and at the end point of that vector we draw the vector v_1. This result is precisely the same as it would be with the wind blowing and the plane flying simultaneously. The resultant velocity is simply the vector connecting the point of origin with the end point. It is easy to see that we would arrive at the same answer if both vectors were drawn from the same origin and the diagonal of the resultant parallelogram were taken as the result, as shown in Fig. 4.5b. Thus, we find that two vectors (in this case, the plane's velocity and the wind's velocity) can be composed into a single resultant vector.

It is also important to understand that a vector can be decomposed into *components.* For example, we may speak of v_0 and v_1 in Fig. 4.5b as the two components of v. The component of v in the direction of the wind is simply v multiplied by the cosine of the angle between v and the direction of the wind. This is a general rule

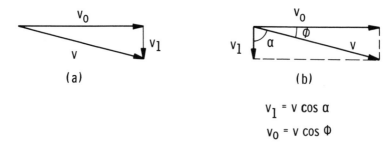

$$v_1 = v \cos \alpha$$
$$v_0 = v \cos \phi$$

Figure 4.5

for finding the component of a vector in a given direction; that is, the component of a vector in a direction making an angle α with the vector is simply the magnitude of the vector multiplied by the cosine of α.

Now, after this rather lengthy digression, let's get back to the motion of a charged particle in a magnetic field. It is found experimentally that a charged particle moving in a magnetic field H experiences a force

$$F = \frac{q}{c} vH \sin \alpha, \tag{4.14}$$

where v is the velocity of the particle, H is the magnetic field, and α is the angle between H and v. The constant c in this equation depends on the units we use to measure the electric charge q and the magnetic field H. If q is expressed in electrostatic units and H in electromagnetic units (gauss), it can be shown that c is numerically equal to the velocity of light, that is, about 3.10^{10} cm/sec. Using the ideas we have been discussing, it is relatively easy to verify that the force is also equal to

$$F = \frac{q}{c} vH_{\perp} = \frac{q}{c} v_{\perp}H, \tag{4.15}$$

where $H_{\perp}$ is the component of H directed perpendicular to the velocity, and $v_{\perp}$ is the component of v directed perpendicular to H.

Previously, we defined the direction of an electric field as that in which a positive charge would move when placed in the field. The magnetic field is similarly defined, but the situation is more complicated. From Eq. 4.14, we know that if the particle has a velocity parallel or antiparallel to the magnetic field, the force on the particle is zero. Thus, we may say that if a particle traveling at a velocity v in a magnetic field experiences *no* force, the magnetic field acts along the path followed by the particle. However, we see immediately that we have only partially defined the direction, because so far the field could be either parallel or antiparallel to the velocity. The choice between these two directions is purely a matter of convention. The accepted convention, outlined in Fig. 4.6, is as follows: If the particle is moving in a direction perpendicular to that of the magnetic field, the force will be a maximum (Eq. 4.14) and is found to be directed perpendicular both to the magnetic field direction and to the velocity vector. Now, if we point the middle finger of the left hand in the direction of mo-

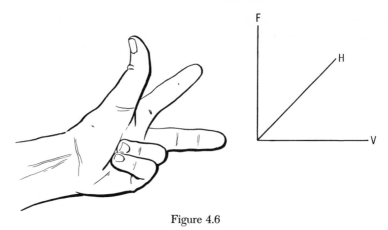

Figure 4.6

tion of a *positive* charge, and the thumb in the direction of the force, the index finger will then be pointing in the direction of the magnetic field. We can now turn the situation around. Having determined the direction of the magnetic field by means of a suitable positive test charge, we can use either Eq. 4.14 or Eq. 4.15 to determine the force exerted on any charged particle. It is clear that since the force is proportional to q, the direction of the force reverses if the sign of q changes.

Let's use a simple case to further explain how a charged particle moves in a magnetic field. First, if the particle is at rest, the force on it is zero, and thus the magnetic field has no effect. If we now allow the electron or particle to move, but only in the direction of the magnetic field, the force is again zero, since there is no component of the field perpendicular to the velocity.

Now consider the situation where the velocity is initially directed perpendicular to the magnetic field. A magnetic field exerts a force on a moving charge directed always at right angles to its velocity. What is the motion of such a charge? Since this force is of the same character as the more familiar centrifugal force, the motion of the charge is circular. Let's examine this idea in more detail.

Suppose we have a particle held by a string fastened at 0, as shown in Fig. 4.7, moving in a circular path of radius r with a speed v. At one instant, the particle is at A; at a time $t = \alpha r/v$ later it is at B, where αr is the length of the arc AB. Although the speed of the particle is the same at both A and B, the direction of the velocity has changed. We can draw a line to denote both the magnitude and direction of the particle's velocity v_A when at A, and similarly v_B when at B. The inset in the upper right of Fig 4.7 shows the velocities v_A and v_B drawn separately, and we see that a velocity δv must be added to v_A in order to attain the velocity v_B. Thus the line δv denotes the change in velocity. Since v_A, v_B, and δv form an isosceles triangle whose apex angle is α, the magnitude of δv is given by

$$\delta v = 2v \sin \frac{\alpha}{2}. \tag{4.16}$$

If α is made very small, it is rather easy to verify from trigometric

tables that $\sin \dfrac{\alpha}{2} \simeq \dfrac{\alpha}{2}$, where α is expressed in radians. Thus,

$$\delta v = \alpha v. \tag{4.17}$$

Since the acceleration is defined as the change in velocity in a time t, and in the present case $t = \alpha r/v$,

$$a = \frac{\delta v}{t} = \frac{v^2 \alpha}{\alpha r} = \frac{v^2}{r}. \tag{4.18}$$

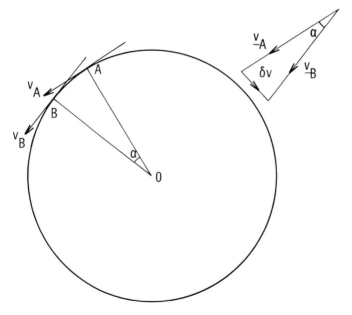

Figure 4.7

In the limiting case, as α approaches zero, it can be seen from Fig. 4.7 that δv is directed at right angles to v, and hence the acceleration is directed toward the center 0 of the circle.

We know from Newton's second law that this acceleration must be caused by a force that the string exerts on the particle. If m is the mass of the particle, the inward force is $F = ma$; this is the *centripetal* force. The particle, in turn, exerts an equal and opposite force (that is, outward) on the string; this is the *centrifugal* force. Thus, if a particle of mass m is to move in a circular path of radius r with a speed v, it must at all times undergo a force

$$F = ma = \frac{mv^2}{r} \qquad (4.19)$$

applied at right angles to its instantaneous direction of motion.

Now let's re-examine the charged particle in a magnetic field. We can conclude from the preceding discussion, especially from Eq. 4.19, that if a particle moves so that a force F is always applied at right angles to its instantaneous velocity, the particle moves in a circular path of radius r, so that

$$r = \frac{mv^2}{F}. \qquad (4.20)$$

Since magnetic force is of the character described, the particle in a magnetic field can be expected to execute circular motion.

THE INFLUENCE OF ELECTRIC AND MAGNETIC FIELDS

Originally we set out to investigate the behavior of a small charged particle, such as an electron or an ion, in electric and magnetic fields. The ideas we have been discussing so far are essential to an understanding of our central theme, electron motion.

As we mentioned earlier, when dealing with particles of atomic or subatomic mass, we can ignore gravitational force, since it is negligible compared to the electromagnetic forces. In the absence of any electric or magnetic field, a particle will move in a straight line, maintaining a constant velocity until it meets some obstacle. But in the presence of an electric field E, a particle of charge q and mass m experiences a force $F = qE$, and an acceleration $a = F/m = qE/m$.

When the field is parallel to the direction of motion, it will either increase or decrease the velocity, depending on the sense of the field. Suppose the field is applied in a direction transverse to that of the motion. In this case, the particle acquires a transverse component of velocity, and thus is deflected from its straight course. Any other situation can be described as a combination of these two by resolving the electric field (a vector) into two perpendicular components, one parallel and one perpendicular to the initial velocity.

Now let's see what happens when a charged particle moves across a small region in which there is a concentrated electric field transverse to the particle velocity, as illustrated in Fig. 4.8. Since the particle moves in a direction perpendicular to the field, it will be deflected. Let's say the width of the region containing the field E is denoted by d, as shown, and the time it takes the particle to cross this region is $t = d/v$. The transverse acceleration is eE/m, so that the transverse velocity acquired is $\delta v = at = (eE/m) \times (d/v)$. The deflection, or change in direction, may be written

$$\tan \Theta = \frac{\delta v}{v} = \frac{eEd}{mv^2}.$$

However, since we know that Θ is small, we may use the approximation that $\tan \Theta = \Theta$, if Θ is expressed in radians. Thus, the angle of deflection is

$$\Theta = \frac{\delta v}{v} = \frac{eEd}{mv^2}. \tag{4.21}$$

Such a localized electric field can be produced by means of a pair of plates (condenser plates) with an electric potential applied across them. We will refer to this arrangement later.

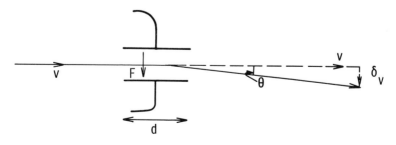

Figure 4.8

The force exerted by a magnetic field differs from that of an electric field in two important respects. First, it is exerted in a direction perpendicular to the field; second, its magnitude depends not only on the magnetic field H, but also on the velocity of the particle (see Eq. 4.14).

When the magnetic field is parallel to the particle velocity, it exerts no force. To calculate the force, let's use the second law from Eq. 4.15 by resolving the velocity into components parallel and perpendicular to the magnetic field. If the parallel velocity vanishes, the particle experiences a force perpendicular to its instantaneous direction of motion. According to the ideas discussed in the preceding section, the particle will execute a circular motion, and the radius r of this circle will be related to $v_\perp$ by Eq. 4.15 and Eq. 4.20, that is,

$$r = mv_\perp \frac{c}{qH}. \qquad (4.22)$$

If the particle also has a velocity component $v_{\parallel}$ parallel to the magnetic field, this component will be unaffected. The particle motion will then be compounded of two motions: a uniform translation in the direction of H, and a circular motion in a plane normal to H, so that the particle would describe a helix on the surface of a cylinder, a path similar to the thread of a screw, as shown in Fig. 4.9a. The axis of the cylinder is parallel to H, and its radius r is given by Eq. 4.22. The radius is determined by H and $v_\perp$, and the pitch of the helix by the ratio of $v_\perp/v_{\parallel}$.

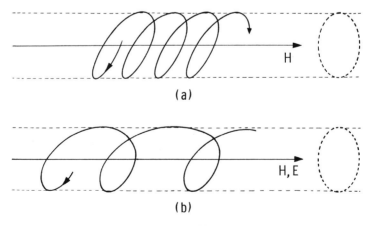

(a)

(b)

Figure 4.9

If an electric field is now applied parallel to the magnetic field, the particle will still travel on the same cylindrical surface, but as $v_\parallel$ will be changed by the electric field, the pitch of the helix will change continuously. This is shown in Fig. 4.9b for the case of acceleration in the direction of $v_\parallel$, so that the pitch increases. When the acceleration is opposed to $v_\parallel$, the pitch decreases as $v_\parallel$ decreases, and the helix turns become tighter; finally, $v_\parallel$ vanishes and then reverses itself so that the direction of the helix also reverses. The pitch then increases continuously, and the helix becomes progressively more open.

Thus, a charged particle can spiral in a magnetic field, and the helix can be extended, compressed, and even reversed by a suitable electric field parallel to H. In the event that the electric field is *not* parallel to H, the resulting path of the particle is far more complicated.

The tendency of charged particles to spiral around magnetic lines of force is of considerable importance. It can be used to guide their motion or to focus them on a spot, as in electron optics. On the geophysical and astrophysical scale, even quite moderate magnetic fields, such as that of the earth, can be of great value in trapping and channeling charged particles. The fact that the radius of the helix, according to Eq. 4.22, is somewhat larger is of little consequence in view of the great distances involved. Thus, charged particles emitted by the sun, or coming from outer space and traveling toward the earth, are caught by the earth's magnetic field high above the stratosphere. They are then constrained to travel mainly along the magnetic lines of force from pole to pole, and are reflected at each pole, thus reversing their spiral motion, as described above. The resulting accumulation of charged particles around the earth is called the Van Allen radiation belt, a region of very dense particle radiation, whose presence was not suspected until its rather recent discovery by high-altitude satellites.

We have seen in Eq. 4.21 that a charged particle is deflected in crossing a region that contains a transverse electric field. A similar deflection can be produced by a transverse magnetic field. If the field is uniform, the particle moves in a circle, but a localized field acts only for a short time, producing a deflection. In Fig. 4.10 a magnetic field H, oriented perpendicular to the plane of the paper, occupies the shaded region of width d. Let's suppose that a charged particle of velocity v spends a time d/v under the influence of field H.

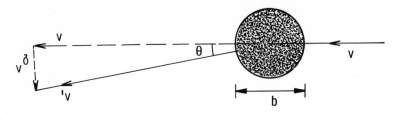

Figure 4.10

According to Eq. 4.15, it will experience a transverse acceleration qHv/mc during that time, and will thus acquire a transverse velocity

$$\delta v = \frac{qHdv}{mc}. \tag{4.23}$$

As before, the angle of its deflection is $\Theta = \delta v/v$, and thus,

$$\Theta = \frac{qHd}{mc}. \tag{4.24}$$

Therefore, when an electron crosses a region that has either a transverse electric or transverse magnetic field, it will be deflected sideways.

So far we have described the essential details of the ways in which charged particles move in electric and magnetic fields. Now let's see how these ideas apply to some real physical situations.

5

Electrons in Test Tubes

WHEN STUDYING the motion of electrons in a gas, we are greatly hindered if they collide too frequently with atoms and molecules. The distance an electron can travel before collision depends not only on the size of each gas molecule, but on the number per unit volume. For example, in a gas at normal temperature and pressure, a typical molecule may have a cross-section dimension equivalent to a sphere of radius 2×10^{-8} cm, and an electron will travel a mean free path of roughly 3×10^{-5} cm before striking a molecule. This does not allow time to study its rectilinear motion and its deflection by electric and magnetic fields, since such observation requires a mean free path of at least a few centimeters.

To circumvent this difficulty, it is necessary to decrease the pressure of the gas, which decreases the number of molecules. In other words, a vacuum is necessary. If the electrons are to travel the required few centimeters, a pressure of say one-millionth of atmosphere is needed at most; that is, a vacuum of 10^{-3} mm Hg. Such pressures are readily attained with modern mechanical pumps. By using a diffusion pump backed by a mechanical pump, it is possible in modern laboratory practice to obtain pressures of 10^{-6} mm Hg. (Normal pressure—one atmosphere—is 760 mm Hg.)

A good vacuum is needed not only to allow the electrons to travel a sufficiently long distance, but also to avoid the occurrence of positively charged gas atoms, or molecules, in concentrations that would produce undesirable electric fields. For many purposes (for example, the vacuum tubes to be discussed later) this represents an even more stringent requirement than that of the mean free path, as far as the quality of the vacuum is concerned.

When an electron travels a distance l in an electric field E, it picks up an amount of energy eEl, where e is the electronic charge. If the electron collides with an atom or molecule, it can impart energy to the atom, knock out another electron, and leave the gas atom in an ionized state. The least amount of energy required for ionization is eI, where I is the ionization potential. This potential, typically of the order of 10 volts, differs for different atoms or molecules. The conditions under which ionization can occur may be calculated roughly by equating the energy required by the electron in a mean free path with the ionization energy, that is,

$$El = I. \tag{5.1}$$

Thus, when $l = 2 \times 10^{-2}$ cm, at a gas pressure of 1 mm Hg, a field of about 500 volts/cm would be required to maintain a gas discharge.

Actually, we have oversimplified the problem, because if an electron has not acquired enough energy in one free path to induce ionization, it can make an *elastic collision*, that is, one that maintains its energy. It then has a good chance of picking up additional energy from the field in its next free path. Therefore, the minimum field necessary to maintain a gas discharge is really somewhat smaller than we calculated, but our crude considerations are accurate enough for the present purpose.

When atoms are excited by electrons of sufficient energy, they store this energy for a while and then emit it in the form of light. This light emission causes the characteristic glow of discharge tubes, which will be described in detail later. The luminosity is created by electrons moving in high electric fields in the presence of a sufficient number of gas particles. The dark spaces in a discharge tube are regions of low electric field. As the gas pressure is decreased, and with it the number of gas particles, the luminous intensity decreases, and the extent of the dark spaces increases. At low enough pressures, only the electrons, or cathode rays, contribute to the conduction process and the glow disappears. We can best study cathode rays under these conditions, and while there is no sharp limit, the pressures needed are as low as 10^{-3} mm Hg, or less.

When electrons travel through a vacuum, they are invisible, of course. Light is emitted only when they strike gas atoms or molecules, or a solid surface such as the wall of the container. In a good vacuum, we can "see" electrons only by the luminosity created when they

(Westinghouse Electric Corporation. Permission of United States Air Force)

An electron beam zone refining furnace with its associated control apparatus. In this system an electron stream, emitted from a hot filament, is accelerated by a potential of several thousand volts toward a vertical rod of tungsten. The heat produced on impact is sufficient to melt a short length of the rod, forming a molten zone which is held in place between the solid portions by its own surface tension. As the rod is moved upward through the hot zone, the tungsten melts and recrystallizes to form a purified single crystal. On the left is a vacuum pump; the vertical cylinder in the middle is the furnace itself; and the apparatus on the right controls the amount of heating and the rate of rod motion.

strike a solid surface and, even at that, not all surfaces are suitable. Metallic surfaces, for example, are generally unsuitable, because a metal contains a large number of highly mobile electrons that impart to the metal its ability to conduct electricity. When an electron strikes a metal surface, its energy is shared with these mobile electrons and, spreading rapidly through the metal, is converted into heat rather than into light. Non-metallic solids, however, are able to receive the energy of incident electrons in a concentrated form at certain special locations, often impurity sites, where the energy can be converted into light. Various substances differ both in the amount and in the color of the light emitted by incident electrons.

In the early work with discharge tubes, the cathode rays struck the glass walls of the vacuum vessel, producing a green fluorescence. The fluorescence produced by glass is not very strong but it can be seen in a semidarkened room. Later experimenters increased the intensity of the fluorescence by coating the inside of the glass with powdered chalk. Today many fluorescent materials are available, and methods have been devised for bonding these materials firmly to the glass. Loosely termed "phosphors," the modern fluorescent materials have a much higher yield, and are used in various types of cathode ray display tubes, such as oscilloscopes, radar, and television screens. Typical materials are zinc sulphide and calcium tungstate, and by introducing certain impurities, it is possible to control the color of the fluorescent light. Even more important, the decay time or duration of the fluorescence can also be controlled. Some applications require the fluorescence to disappear quickly; others demand the radiation that follows the arrival of the burst of electrons to last a little longer.

Up to this point, we have simply assumed that we have electrons in a vacuum, without questioning how they were introduced or if the process can be controlled in some way. Let's see what actually happens.

In a gaseous discharge, electrons are produced by the process of ionization, which we have already discussed. Furthermore, in a discharge tube, some of the positive ions can be attracted toward the negative electrode (the cathode) and as they strike the metal surface they eject electrons from the cathode. This is a very suitable method for obtaining high-intensity beams, but it has certain disadvantages. The electrons are produced in a region of relatively poor

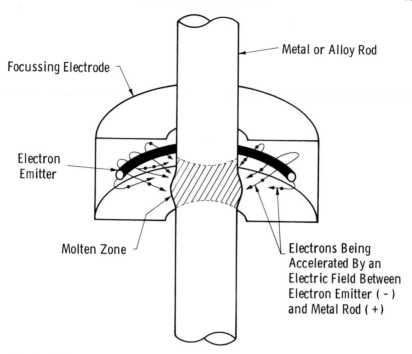

Focussing Electrode

Metal or Alloy Rod

Electron Emitter

Molten Zone

Electrons Being Accelerated By an Electric Field Between Electron Emitter (-) and Metal Rod (+)

A sketch of the geometry of the molten zone and the heater in the electron beam zone refining system. The electron emitter is made several thousand volts negative with respect to the rod, and the electrons striking the rod melt the cross-hatched region. In order not to impede the electron flow, a good vacuum must be maintained in the system. A particular advantage of this technique is its cleanliness; very little impurity content is produced in the melt, and crystals of high purity and perfection result.

vacuum and, although possible, it is rather difficult to pass an electron beam through a narrow orifice from a gaseous region into a high-vacuum region, as shown schematically in Fig. 5.1. Here electrons are ejected from the cathode C, because of the bombardment by positive ions. Most strike the anode A, but some pass through the narrow orifice into the vacuum space at the left. The gas (suitably hydrogen) in the discharge tube is at a pressure of 10^{-3} mm Hg. In a good vacuum, however, it is possible to extract electrons from a metal surface without the need of positive ions, either by photoelectric emission or thermionic emission.

As we mentioned before, a metal contains a large number of mobile electrons which are bound not to any particular atom but to

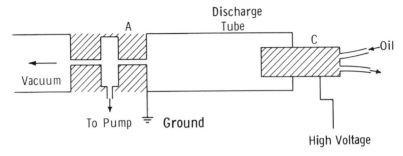

Figure 5.1

the metal as a whole. Although they can move from one region of the metal to another, they are confined to the material itself by an effective barrier. To overcome this barrier and be able to leave the metal, the electrons must have considerable energy; the amount required is called the *work function,* denoted by W.

In the photoelectric effect, light (either visible or ultraviolet) falls on the metal surface, and the light's energy can be imparted to an electron. If the electron thus gains more energy than an amount W, it can break through the confining barrier and leave the metal. In the case of thermionic emission, the electrons acquire thermal energy when the temperature of the metal is raised, and the kinetic energy of an occasional electron may be greater than the average thermal energy. In this event, if the electron happens to be near the surface of the metal at the time and its kinetic energy exceeds W, it has a good chance of escaping from the surface. As the temperature increases, there is a sharp increase in the number of such chances of escape, resulting in an increase in the thermionic emission.

Thermionic emission is widely used to produce electrons in all kinds of vacuum tubes. Although photoelectric emission is usually less convenient, it is used in special cases when the over-riding consideration is good control of the emitted electron beam. It is also the basic mechanism of photocells, devices in which the photoelectric emission of electrons yields an electric current that is a measure of the amount of light falling on a sensitive area. However, we will deal only with thermionic emission in the following discussion.

A heated metal emits electrons from its surface. The hotter the metal, the larger the number of electrons emitted per unit area and time. But it is not enough that electrons simply leave the metal; they

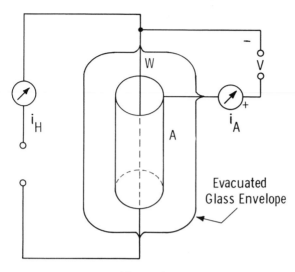

Figure 5.2

must also be able to move away from the emitting surface. If a sufficient number remain just outside the metal surface, they will hinder, or even prevent, the subsequent emission of further electrons, because of the repulsive action of their charge. For thermionic emission to proceed, the metal surface must be in a vacuum so that the electrons are not bounced back by collisions with gas atoms. There must also be an electric field to remove electrons from the immediate vicinity of the surface after they have been emitted.

A typical experimental arrangement for studying thermionic emission is shown schematically in Fig. 5.2. In this device, a tungsten wire (W) is surrounded by a cylindrical metal anode (A), and both wire and anode are in an evacuated glass container. The wire is heated to a glow by a current (i_H) passing through it. A potential difference (V) is applied between the cathode (the wire) and the anode. A meter records the current (i_A) flowing into the anode; this current is equal to that produced by the electrons flowing from the cathode to the anode in the vacuum space. For this experiment to be meaningful, the vacuum must be good enough so that the positive ions do not contribute appreciably to the current, which means it must be better than 10^{-3} mm Hg.

In Fig. 5.3, we see the typical result of such an experiment. Of course, the details depend on the geometry of the arrangement

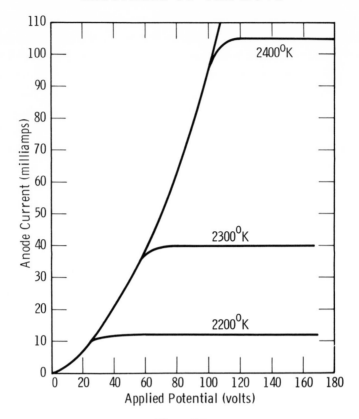

Figure 5.3

and on the nature of the emitting surface. The anode current (i_A) is plotted against the applied voltage (V); a series of curves is obtained, one for each heater current (i_H), and all curves merge into a common curve for low values of V. Different values of the heater current correspond to different temperatures of the wire, and the temperatures, expressed in Kelvin (degrees centigrade $+273$), are marked on the curves.

It appears that two factors limit the anode current: the rate at which electrons leave the surface, and the rate at which they are removed from the immediate vicinity of the wire. Let's first deal with the second factor.

If the applied voltage is in the reverse sense, as in Fig. 5.2, no current flows because an electron, after it leaves the wire, has insufficient energy to overcome the potential difference between the wire and the outer electrode (now at a potential that tends to repel electrons). The emitted electrons are then trapped in the space surrounding the wire, and will tend to return into the wire. Furthermore, they will block the emission of more electrons. Let's suppose that the anode is at a positive potential, but the potential difference is not large. The emitted electrons will now be drawn toward the anode, but at any time an appreciable number will be near the wire. These electrons have a net negative charge, which will act on any further electrons emitted. In other words, the high electron density around the wire will tend to reduce the action of the electric field, due to the externally applied potential difference. Using advanced methods, it is possible to calculate how the effective electric field determines the motion of the emitted electrons, how their motion determines the distribution of electric charge around the wire, and how this charge distribution, in turn, determines the electric field. Once this problem is solved, it is then possible to relate the current of electrons leaving the wire (i_A) to the applied potential difference V, and find that

$$i_A \text{ varies as } V^{3/2}, \tag{5.2}$$

the constant of proportionality depending on the geometry of the arrangement.

However, this treatment assumes that the metal surface can supply electrons at an unlimited rate, and that the current is limited only by the space charge mechanism just described. As the applied potential is increased, there must come a stage at which the space-charge limited current would exceed the electron current the surface is able to emit, and even if V is increased beyond that point, the current i_A cannot be further increased. This is illustrated in Fig. 5.3, where i_A tends to a constant value at large values of V for such fixed value of heater current (or surface temperature). This current, limited by the ability of the metal surface to emit electrons, is called the *saturation current*. Operation in which all the emitted electrons are withdrawn is usually said to be *emission limited* in contrast to the earlier case, which is said to be *space charge limited*.

The saturation current (per unit area of emitting surface) increases very sharply with increased temperature of the wire. In Fig. 5.3, for example, we see that a rise of 100 centigrade degrees increases the saturation current by roughly a factor of 3. This current also depends on the work function W. The lower W, the easier it is for an electron to leave the metal, and the greater will be the saturation current. Indeed, it has been shown that this current depends on the ratio of T/W, where T is the absolute temperature (degrees Kelvin). The choice of a suitable thermionic emitter depends on finding a material with as low a value of W as possible, since there is a practical limit to the highest temperatures at which a thermionic emitter can be operated. Too high a temperature has an adverse effect on the mechanical stability of the cathode. Frequently, substances with low values of the work function are mechanically unsuitable; that is, they cannot maintain their shape very well at elevated temperatures. However, by coating a metal such as nickel, which has good mechanical properties at high temperatures, with a low work function material, the advantages of both are combined. Thus, practically useful thermionic emitters have been constructed from pure tungsten, from thoriated tungsten (containing one to two percent thorium oxide, heat-treated in such a way that thorium atoms accumulate on the surface in an adsorbed layer one atom thick), and from metals such as nickel coated with barium oxide or strontium oxide.

THE CATHODE RAY TUBE

The principles of electron behavior we have been discussing in the preceding section are all embodied in the operation of the cathode ray tube. In this device, free electrons are emitted from the cathode and accelerated through the evacuated interior by a potential difference of several thousand volts between the cathode and the anode, the latter being a phosphor on the glass face of the tube. This phosphor fluoresces or produces light wherever it is struck by the electron stream. A familiar example of this device is a television picture tube.

The various components of a typical cathode ray tube are shown schematically in Fig. 5.4. Let's examine its construction and see how it operates. The electron gun produces a beam of electrons which strikes the screen at one spot. This beam can be deflected by the two sets of deflection plates. When a voltage is applied between the two plates D_1, it sets up an electric field in the intervening space, and the electrons are deflected vertically, moving either up or down depending on the sense of the field, as mentioned earlier. Another set of

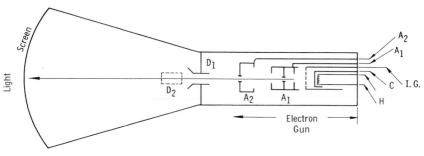

Figure 5.4

plates D_2 produces deflections at right angles to the first set, that is, horizontally.

Although the principles of the electron gun described here are simple enough, the actual design is far from simple. For our present discussion, however, it is unnecessary to explain such highly complex matters as the geometry of the anodes, or the choice of the proper voltages, and so on, to produce an intense narrow beam.

Referring again to Fig. 5.4, the cathode C, heated by an electric filament heater H, emits electrons. In early tube designs, the cathode itself was used as the heater, but in most modern designs, the heater is electrically separate from the emitting cathode, although in thermal contact with it so that the cathode is heated. A perforated electrode or grid, marked I.G. (intensity grid), controls the electric field just outside the cathode surface. As mentioned in the preceding section, such a field controls the number of electrons that are pulled away from the cathode, provided the current is below the saturation level; thus, a small voltage applied to the intensity grid controls the beam current, and therefore the brightness of the luminous spot on the screen. While still at low energy, the electrons pass the intensity grid, and are accelerated in the space between I.G. and the first anode A_1 by a substantial potential difference, typically of a few thousand volts. Further acceleration occurs between A_1 and A_2. Each of these anodes has a central hole which serves to define a narrow beam, and the purpose of the anode arrangement is to collect as large a fraction as possible of the electrons leaving the cathode, pass them through the hole in A_1, and then through A_2, so that a narrow beam results. Once the electrons have passed A_2, they find themselves in an essentially field-free space (except for the fields of the deflector plates), and therefore they travel in a straight line to the screen, where they produce a luminous spot. This implies that the anode and the screen must be at the same potential, and since the screen should be grounded for safe and convenient operation, it is usually the cathode that is at a high negative potential.

In the arrangement depicted here, which is by no means unique, the anode consists of two parts, A_1 and A_2, at different potentials. Of course, it is the potential difference between A_2 and C that determines the terminal velocity of the electrons. The potential of A_1 controls the focus of the beam.

Returning now to the function of the cathode ray tube, we notice that a voltage across the plates D_1 causes the spot to shift vertically, and a voltage across D_2 results in a horizontal shift. By suitably varying these two voltages with time, the spot can be made to trace out a pattern. When the two voltages vary in an oscillatory manner, and the two frequencies bear a simple numerical relation to each other, the pattern traced by the spot is stable and frequently repeated. Because of the finite decay time of the fluorescence and the persistence of visual impressions, this stable pattern is visible and stationary, even if the electric oscillations causing it are of far too high frequency for visual perception. In this way, the cathode ray tube is used as an oscilloscope. A "saw-tooth" voltage is applied across the horizontal plates so that the spot moves steadily from one side to the other, and returns almost instantaneously. If, at the same time, some oscillatory voltage is applied across the vertical plates and the repeat frequency of the saw-tooth pattern is adjusted to the repeat frequency of the vertical voltage, the resulting stable pattern on the screen is a representation of the voltage on the vertical plates as a function of time. In other words, there is a picture of the wave-form of the vertical voltage, as illustrated in Fig. 5.5.

The beam of the cathode ray tube shown in Fig. 5.4 is deflected by an electric field. As we have said before, it is also possible to use a magnetic field for this purpose by passing a current through a coil on the outside of the neck of the tube, near the deflector plates. The magnetic field thus produced in the path of the beam deflects the beam sideways, perpendicular to the direction of the magnetic field. The magnetic method of deflection is often preferred, because the coils generating the field are external to the tube, while deflector

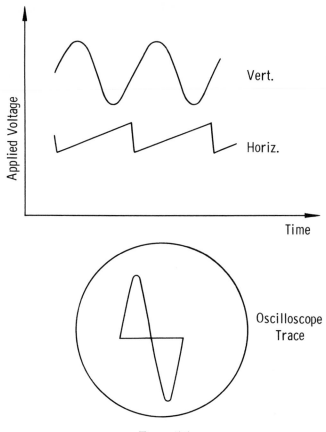

Figure 5.5

plates must be built into the tube itself and cannot subsequently be moved. Furthermore, when large deflections are required, high voltages are needed on the deflector plates, comparable to the difference between the anode and the cathode potentials. It is inconvenient to apply such high voltages at the plates.

Cathode ray oscilloscopes are very useful and convenient tools, widely used in laboratories and electronic workshops. An oscilloscope also serves as a component of many electronic devices, for example, the display screen of a radar installation. The cathode ray tube is found in most homes today; the family without television is rare.

The operation of a television display tube differs slightly from that of the cathode ray oscilloscope. The beam is deflected to trace out a series of closely spaced horizontal lines, called the *raster*, and the entire frame is repeated thirty times a second. The picture is generated by varying the intensity of the beam continuously as the raster is traced out. Intensity is controlled by a high-frequency signal voltage applied to the intensity control electrode. In this case, the deflections that trace out the raster are produced by magnetic coils, for the reasons given above, and one or more coaxial field coils are used to assist the focusing of the beam.

Let's now consider the experiments that throw light on the electronic charge and mass. The history of this subject has been described in Chapter Three, but the basic principles of these measurements remain unchanged, although today the results are more precise and obtained with greater ease.

As long as we study the motion of electrons in electric and magnetic fields, we obtain only information about e/m, the ratio between the charge and the mass of the electron, because these fields exert forces on the electron proportional to e, but the acceleration due to a force F is F/m, and thus proportional to e/m. However, experiments that merely measure the path of an electron beam in a given electric field are not sufficient, since a knowledge of the path does not provide information about the velocity of the electrons. Broadly speaking, there are two methods to determine e/m.

In the first one, the velocity of a beam of electrons is determined by a pair of suitable shutters, the electrons having been accelerated by a known potential difference V. The kinetic energy of the electrons then equals their change in potential energy; that is,

$$\tfrac{1}{2}mv^2 = eV. \tag{5.3}$$

If the velocity v has been directly determined by the time lag in the shutters that allow electrons to pass, the ratio e/m can be deduced. Unfortunately, however, direct measurements of the electron velocity are difficult to perform and the results are not very precise. It is possible to use as shutters a mechanical system in rotation, such as rotating disks perforated with slits, or else an intermittent or time-varying magnetic field, highly localized, which prevents the beam from passing.

The second method, first used in 1873, is a comparison of the deflection of a given beam (that is, electrons of some fixed velocity) by an electric field, with the deflection produced by a magnetic field.

According to Eq. 4.21, a transverse electric field causes a deflection of an electron of velocity v given by

$$\theta = A \frac{e}{v^2 m}, \qquad (5.4)$$

where A depends, in a known way, on the strength of the field and its lateral extent. Similarly, the deflection due to a transverse magnetic field is, from Eq. 4.23,

$$\theta' = A' \frac{e}{vcm}, \qquad (5.5)$$

where c is the velocity of light, and A' is likewise determined by the geometry and strength of the magnetic field. By measuring both the electric and magnetic deflections of the same electron beam, it is possible to determine both the velocity v of the electrons and the value of e/m. Such an experiment is readily performed on a modern cathode ray tube, which has deflection plates of known geometry, and to which a magnetic field can be applied from the outside.

As a variant of this method, electrons can be accelerated from rest through a known potential difference V, and then deflected magnetically. The ratio e/m and the value of v can be determined by combining Eq. 5.3 and Eq. 5.5. In essence, this was the method used in 1897 by W. Kaufmann, who was the first to determine e/m with reasonable precision. The method involving deflections by both electric and magnetic fields was used by Wilhelm Wien in 1898, and later by Alexander Classen in 1908.

According to the best measurements today, the value of e/m is

$$e/m = 0.528 \times 10^{18} \text{ esu per gram}$$
$$= 1.761 \times 10^8 \text{ coulomb per gram} \qquad (5.6)$$

(esu refers to electrostatic units). From this quantity, we can readily deduce the velocity v of an electron accelerated from rest through a potential difference V, using the relation in Eq. 5.3. Table 5A gives a few representative values, both in cm/sec and in fractions of the velocity of light. It should be noted that the relation in Eq. 5.3 fails as v approaches the velocity of light. This is a consequence of the theory of relativity, and for this reason we have not given the velocities of electrons of energy in excess of 10,000 electron volts, that is, electrons accelerated through potentials over 10,000 volts.

TABLE 5A

*Velocity of electrons after acceleration from rest through
a potential difference V.*

V (in volts)	v (in 10^9 cm/sec)	v/c
10	0.188	0.00626
40	0.375	0.0125
100	0.594	0.0198
500	1.326	0.0442
1000	1.878	0.0626
2000	2.649	0.0883
5000	4.14	0.138
10,000	5.85	0.195

THE SCALE OF THE ATOMIC WORLD

Although the atomicity of matter was part of the general scientific
knowledge of the nineteenth century, explaining many regularities in
chemistry and providing a natural explanation of numerous thermodynamic properties through the kinetic theory of gases, for a long
time it proved impossible to deduce the size (or mass) of the atom. It
was concluded that an atom must be such an exceedingly small entity
that usual methods were too insensitive for its measurement. As long
as known techniques were confined to the measurement of macroscopic (bulk) properties, nothing could be deduced about the scale of
the atomic world; it was possible to derive only ratios of microscopic
(atomic) quantities. The elucidation of this mystery had to await the
appearance of sensitive and refined techniques for detecting and
measuring individual atomic properties or events. This was also true
of the "atom" of electricity, the electron. In early experiments,
described in Chapter Three, only the integrated effects of many electrons were observed; the number of electrons involved was not determined. Thus, only the ratio e/m could be found, but not the electronic
charge e or the electron mass m separately.

A knowledge of the magnitude of the electronic charge also provides a knowledge of the atomic masses, and thus the entire scale of
atomic properties, or vice versa. For example, by measuring the amount
of material deposited electrolytically by a known charge, it is possible to
deduce the ratio of e, the electronic charge, to M, the atomic mass of

the particular element used. (In this connection it is interesting to recall that the international unit of electric charge, the coulomb, was defined for many years in terms of the mass of silver deposited electrolytically by the passage of that charge.)

It turns out that the electric effects of the charge of a single electron, although not large, are considerably larger than various non-electric effects due to one atom, and the electron therefore provides a good handle for determining the atomic magnitudes. Thus, the direct determination of the electronic charge by Robert A. Millikan was the first to yield reasonable precision in determining Avogadro's number and all other associated quantities. However, Millikan's work was preceded by a number of rough determinations of the size of an atom, and in their day these were very significant, since they provided some answer to the important question of atomic scale. Furthermore, they afforded vital information for the design of later and more refined experiments.

The kinetic theory of gases, for example, teaches us that the viscosity of a gas is related to the free path traveled by an atom before it strikes another atom, or before it collides with the walls in fine capillaries and at low pressures. This mean free path, determined from viscosity measurements, is thus a rough measure of atomic dimensions. Another example of such an estimate of atomic dimensions is Jean Perrin's study of the distribution of small particles of a colloidal suspension as a function of height. The kinetic theory of gases states that the mean energy of any atom per degree of freedom is the same at a given temperature. By treating each colloidal particle (of known size) as an atom, its mean kinetic energy, and thus the mean kinetic energy of any atom, can be determined from the mean potential energy. From the known thermal energy of a real gas, it is thus possible to deduce the number of atoms the gas contains.

Millikan's oil drop method, described in detail in Chapter Three, is based on the following principle: If the motion of a particle of mass M and charge q is observed in an electric field so that the ratio of q/M is determined, q can be calculated provided M is known. By using a charged oil droplet, minute but large compared to atomic size, M can be deduced, and thus q. Since the electric forces due to an elementary charge are very much larger than other forces, the gravitational force on a droplet can be made comparable to electric forces on a single electron due to moderate fields. Thus, the conditions of the experiment can be selected so that drops charged with only a small number of electrons can be studied. If the charges on many drops are measured, it turns out that q is always an integral multiple of an elementary charge e, which is identified with the electronic charge.

The ratio q/M is measured by comparing the force of a known electric field with the force of gravity. The mass of each droplet is determined from its terminal velocity of fall in air; this velocity depends on the size of the droplet and the viscosity of the air. Thus the motion of a charged particle is observed, both under the influence of an electric field and when falling free, and it is possible to deduce q/M and M respectively, and thus q. The value of the electronic charge is $e = 4.80 \times 10^{-10}$ esu $= 1.60 \times 10^{-19}$ coulomb, which makes Avogadro's number $N_O = 6.02 \times 10^{23}$.

The method that yields the greatest precision for these values at present is x-ray diffraction. Atoms in a crystal form a regular array, and if the interatomic spacing is known, the number of atoms in a given amount of crystalline material can be calculated, and thus also Avogadro's number. The lattice spacing of a crystal, in terms of the wavelength of x rays, can be determined by using the crystal as a diffraction grating. The angle of diffraction yields the ratio of lattice spacing to wavelength. Soft x rays (long-wave) can also be diffracted by a ruled grating and their wavelength determined by the line density of the grating. However, the x rays must be diffracted at almost grazing incidence, since their wavelength is much shorter than the grid spacing.

VACUUM TUBES

When current flows through any material, even a good conductor, it experiences a certain amount of resistance. Therefore, a potential difference is needed to keep a current flowing in the face of the frictional forces exerted on the carriers of electric charge. In a great many situations, the current flow is proportional to the potential difference applied (Ohm's law), and the resistance R of a material of some configuration is given by

$$i = \frac{V}{R}. \tag{5.7}$$

The direction of the current flow is determined by the direction of the applied voltage, and the resistive material has no directional bias; the resistance to current flow in one direction is exactly equal to the resistance in the reversed sense.

In many electrotechnical applications, particularly in the field of electrical communication, signalling, and control, there is a profound need for devices which will allow flow of current only in one direction, or at least strongly favor flow in a given direction, and will allow the current to be easily and rapidly modified by the application of a controlling voltage. Both functions can be fulfilled by the vacuum tube. It is a measure of the success of this device that today the science and technology dealing with signal and control circuits is referred to simply as "electronics."

Since the flow of electricity in a good vacuum is due entirely to the motion of electrons introduced into the vacuum by an electrode, asymmetric flow characteristics of a vacuum tube can be attained by an asymmetry in the shape or character of the electrodes. It is easy to insure that one electrode is more efficient than the other in emitting electrons, and this will allow current to flow preferentially in one direction, so that in effect the vacuum tube acts as a valve. This is accomplished by making one electrode of a material with a low work function, and keeping it hotter than the other. In some special cases, heat is produced by passing a current through the electrode, but a more common method is to heat the cathode by means of a supplementary electric heater, as in the case of the electron gun we have already described.

The device mentioned earlier in this chapter and illustrated in Fig. 5.2 is actually a rudimentary vacuum tube that insures preferential current flow in one direction. The central wire emits electrons when it is heated, and if the outer cylindrical electrode is at a positive potential, these electrons are drawn away from the cathode so that current flows. Under reverse bias, however, the current is quite small, practically zero, as indicated in Fig. 5.3.

Such a two-electrode vacuum tube is called a *diode*. As we will see later, however, this term is used for any device that serves as a rectifier. We will meet it again in Chapter Seven, when we discuss various semiconductor devices and their operation. But for the time being, the term refers to the two-electrode vacuum tube. For compactness

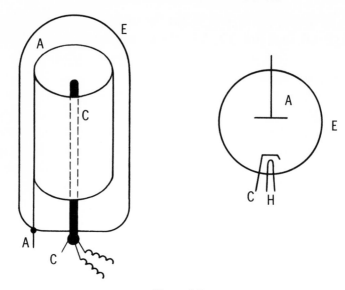

Figure 5.6

and operational convenience, diodes are constructed somewhat dif-
ferently from the device illustrated in Fig. 5.2, although the principle
of operation is the same. The diode construction shown in Fig. 5.6 is
typical, but only one of several variations. The actual physical
arrangement is shown at the left of the diagram; at the right is a
schematic representation used in circuit diagrams. There are two electrodes, the cathode C and the anode A, enclosed in an evacuated container or envelope E, which may be either glass or metal. The
cathode is usually oxide-coated and has an internal heating filament.
The tube is frequently mounted on a synthetic resin socket which is
not shown in this diagram. The tube is evacuated and sealed during
manufacture, and vacuum tightness dictates the choice of material for
the envelope. Since the vacuum must be maintained for the lifetime
of the tube, the envelope has to be impervious to gas diffusion and it
must not liberate gas in the course of time. The envelope must also
be of suitable material to allow vacuum-tight seals where conductors
from the electrodes to the outside pass through the envelope.

The cathode is electrically heated and coated with oxide for good
thermionic emission. In most modern tubes, the heater filaments are
enclosed in a hollow space within the cathode and electrically
insulated from it. Sometimes the cathode also serves as the heater

element, as shown in Fig. 5.2. When the tube is represented schematically in circuit diagrams (Fig. 5.6), the heater connections are omitted, since it is regarded as self-evident that every vacuum tube has a heater for the cathode.

The operation of the diode is completely analogous to the case discussed earlier in this chapter; the current flows only when the anode is at a positive potential relative to the cathode. Thus, when an alternating potential is applied to the simple rectifying circuit shown in Fig. 5.7, the current flows only during the positive half-cycle, that is, when the anode is at a positive potential. No current flows during the negative half-cycle. The voltage across the resistor R, therefore, is sometimes positive and sometimes zero, but never negative. The diode converts an alternating voltage into one which, although not constant, has an average value that is positive. By means of other circuit elements (not shown in Fig. 5.7) involving an inductance, this

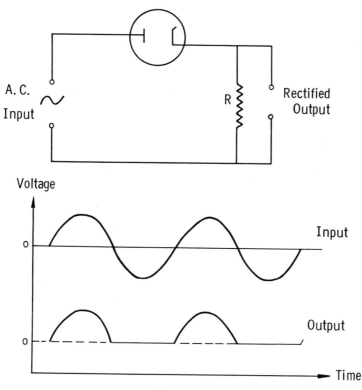

Figure 5.7

voltage can be smoothed out so that it is almost steady, if this is required. This smoothing process is unnecessary in some applications, such as the rectification of radio-frequency signals as part of their detection. The circuit shown is only one of several possible rectifying circuits incorporating diodes. By using a tandem arrangement of two or four diodes, it is possible to obtain more efficiency and smoother output.

Usually we want to make the electron current in the diode as large as possible during the favorable half-cycle. Therefore, the geometry is chosen so that there will be a strong electric field near the cathode, which draws off all the electrons as soon as they are emitted; that is, we operate the diode in the emission limited mode. If the electric field is not large enough to remove the electrons quickly, a space charge builds up outside the cathode, and this inhibits the current flow. Thus, in Fig. 5.3 the current is less than the saturation current for sufficiently low voltages, that is, for low enough values of the electric field just outside the cathode surface.

In a vacuum tube, the electric field at the cathode can be controlled by regulating the potential difference between the anode and the cathode. However, it is more convenient to control this electric field by introducing a third electrode. In such a device, called a *triode,* the third electrode is a grid placed close to the cathode, as shown in Fig. 5.8. This diagram illustrates one possible electrode arrangement of a triode, with the cathode in the center. The anode is the outer cylinder and the grid is in the form of a helix closely surrounding the cathode. On the right, a triode is shown schematically.

Usually vacuum triodes are operated in the space charge limited mode so that a space charge of electrons builds up between the cathode and the grid. The function of the grid is to control the rate at which electrons are withdrawn from the space charge region to go to the anode. This control is achieved by applying a voltage to the grid which, in turn, affects the electric field in the space charge region. Because the grid is close to the cathode, a small potential difference between the two will have a substantial effect on this electric field and thus on the current flowing to the anode. The grid must be adequately wide-meshed so that most of the electrons will pass through it as they travel from cathode to anode. The grid voltage is normally negative with respect to the cathode, so that

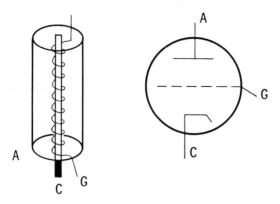

Figure 5.8

no electrons can reach the grid and no current flows in the grid circuit.

In all signal or control applications, information is carried through the system by the manner in which a voltage or current varies as a function of time. Such a signal is continuously attenuated by dissipative processes, either in the circuit, or inherent in the transmission of information over long distances, such as the dispersal of radio waves, losses in a telephone line, and so forth. Therefore, it is always necessary to regenerate the signal by amplifying it, and thus a device is needed that faithfully reproduces the signal with enhanced amplitude.

This important function is accomplished by the triode. Since the voltage on the grid controls the current through the tube, a

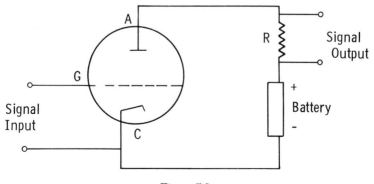

Figure 5.9

variation in the grid voltage as a function of time causes a like variation in the anode current. When this current, also called the *plate current,* passes through a resistance R, as shown in Fig. 5.9, it causes a variation in the potential across R, which is a reproduction of the grid voltage as a function of time but can be enhanced in magnitude, provided R is chosen correctly. Amplification is possible because very little power is dissipated in the grid circuit since no current flows out of the grid, but more power is associated with the output signal; this power is taken from the battery or other power supply which maintains the potential difference between the anode and the cathode.

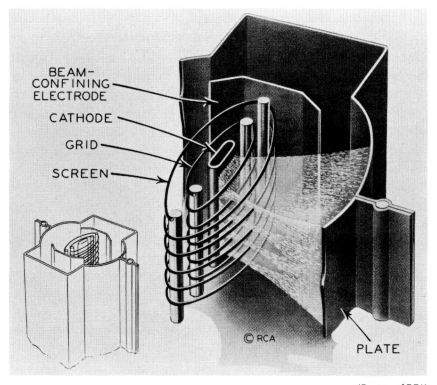

(Courtesy of RCA)

Cutaway view of an important type of vacuum tube called the *beam power pentode,* typified by the 6L6. The wires of the concentric grid and screen are aligned so that electrons from the cathode, passing between the negative grid wires, for the most part also pass between the wires of the positive screen, thus resulting in a tube with low screen current.

A triode is a very versatile device for amplification and for the generation of high-frequency alternating currents, that is, currents of higher frequencies than those attainable with rotating machinery, as well as for various other functions. A variety of circuit designs are used, and in many cases the simple circuit of Fig. 5.9 would be quite unsuitable, particularly when faithful reproduction and stability are required. Without going into any of the details, we mention in passing that for some purposes more complicated vacuum tubes have been designed. Those with four electrodes (two grids, cathode and plate) are called *tetrodes,* and tubes with five electrodes (three grids) are called *pentodes.*

Vacuum tubes, particularly diodes and triodes, have opened up the broad field of electronics. The invention of these devices, with their ability to amplify very weak signals and detect high frequency signals by rectifying them, has within a few decades completely transformed man's means of communication and drastically altered the way he carries on business, spends his leisure hours, and wages war.

PART 3

Trapped in the Solid

6

Bound
−But Not Immobile

WE HAVE ASSUMED so far that the electron has little or no interaction with its surroundings; in other words, we have been discussing only the *free* electron. This means that the sole forces on the electron we have needed to take into consideration are those due to electric and magnetic fields. Now that we have some understanding of the properties of free electrons and have seen how these properties may be used for practical purposes, we can go a step farther and investigate the behavior of electrons when the interaction with their environment is strong; that is, we want to know how electrons behave in solids.

Loosely speaking, solids may be divided into two broad categories—metals and insulators. In referring to pure materials, a distinction between these two may be made in the following way: a metal has low electrical resistivity even at the lowest temperatures; an insulator, on the other hand, has very high electrical resistivity under the same conditions. Obviously, this is not a very precise classification; it is often difficult to classify a given material even when its properties are known. But as we go along, the truly fundamental difference between a metal and an insulator will become apparent, although our major emphasis will be on the insulator in the following discussion.

ATOMS AND MOLECULES

Since the atom is the building block of the solid, let's begin our story with the simplest, the hydrogen atom. This is composed of one positively charged proton, forming the nucleus, and one negatively charged electron. The charges of the proton and the electron precisely balance each other, and therefore the hydrogen atom is electrically neutral. We can see in Fig. 6.1a, which represents this atom schematically, that the nucleus (proton) is at the center of a dark cloud. This cloud indicates the negative charge of the orbiting electron. By picturing the electron in this way, we do not mean to imply that it is not a particle; we only indicate that the electron's continually overlapping orbits about the nucleus are such that it

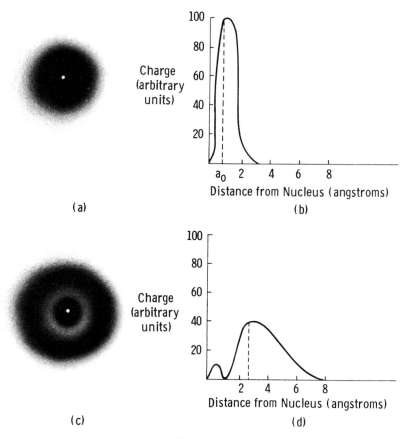

(a)

(b)

(c)

(d)

Figure 6.1

spends most of the time in the darkest areas, the least time in the lighter areas. Now, if we were able to start from the nucleus and, moving outward radially, measure the total charge in each successive spherical shell, or orbit, we would find the result given in Fig. 6.1b. This means that although the electron may roam around, so to speak, it spends most of the time at a distance a_0 from the nucleus. (This distance a_0 is approximately .5 Å (angstroms), and one Å $= 10^{-8}$ cm.)

Let's jump several steps now, and examine a container of hydrogen gas at a very high temperature. Much of the gas will be in the form of hydrogen *molecules*, about which we will say more later. In addition, however, there will be a large number of hydrogen *atoms* present. If we study the distribution of a number of these atoms, we may be surprised to discover that although many have the distribution of Fig. 6.1b, with a maximum at a_0, there are also many others with new charge distributions, such as those shown in Fig. 6.1d. (This figure is represented pictorially by Fig. 6.1c.) However, there are fewer of these than of the atoms having the distribution of Fig. 6.1b. In short, we find a great many different charge distributions. For our present purposes we want to list these in an order such that the maximum in the charge distribution is farther away from the nucleus in each successive distribution than it was in the preceding one.

First, what can we say about these hydrogen atoms? We know that an attractive force exists between the negatively charged electron and the positively charged nucleus. This being the case, we would expect the charge distribution of Fig. 6.1b to be the most "comfortable" for the atom, because here the electron is closest to the nucleus, on the average. This is called the *ground state*, or state of lowest energy. With the distributions of Fig. 6.1d, the electron is farther away from the nucleus on the average. This *excited state* is one of higher energy, which implies that in order to get into the state of Fig. 6.1d, the atom of Fig. 6.1b must be excited by receiving a "shot" of energy. The necessary energy may come from many different sources. For example, the atom can receive energy from a collision with another atom, or from being exposed to light. In hydrogen gas we find higher and higher excited states, and it is not surprising that some hydrogen atoms can be excited to such a degree that their electrons are simply torn away from the nuclei. When this happens, we say the atoms have been *ionized*.

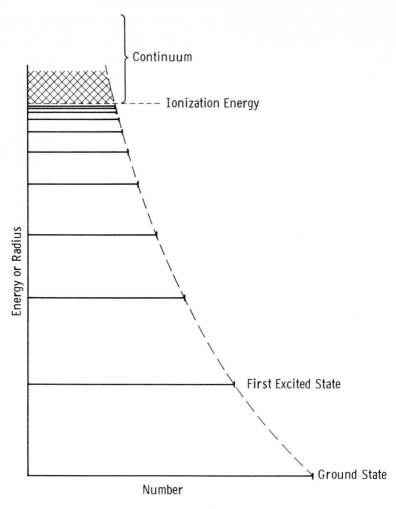

Figure 6.2

Since a graph often helps to clarify points that have been made, we can summarize our discussion with the graph shown in Fig. 6.2. The horizontal axis gives the relative number of atoms in each state. Vertically, we plot the energy, or the average radius, of the state. (We have already seen that these two quantities are proportional to each other.) If we now make the appropriate studies, we observe that the largest number of atoms is in the lowest energy state, and the number per state decreases continually as the energy of each state is increased. We find the fewest atoms in the state where the electron and the proton are completely separated, and at rest with respect to each other. This is labeled the *ionization energy*. Can there be even higher energy states than this? Indeed, there can be, for not only can the electron be free of the nucleus, it can also have a velocity of its own and thereby a kinetic energy. It is apparent that as the kinetic energy of the free electron increases, we are describing higher and higher energy states. In the diagram, these states are shown above the ionization energy, and they are labeled *continuum*, for reasons that will soon be apparent.

We must now face a rather difficult point. There is a qualitative difference between the state of the ionized atom and that of the un-ionized atom. When the atom is ionized, its electron may have *any* kinetic energy, starting from zero. In technical language we say that there is a "continuum" of such states. However, we notice that in Fig. 6.2 there are only certain energy levels drawn below the point of ionization, and this must mean that only specific energies are allowed. We say, in this case, that the energy levels are *quantized*.

On the basis of Newtonian mechanics, it was impossible to understand the idea of quantized energy levels, since one would expect to find a continuum of levels for both cases, the ionized and the un-ionized. With the accumulation of scientific evidence, it became obvious that the mechanics of Newton would have to be revised. This revision culminated in the work of E. Schroedinger of Austria, and W. Heisenberg of Germany, two physicists who developed modern quantum mechanics. It will be unnecessary here to delve into this rather complicated science, but we should note that it provides an understanding of systems such as the hydrogen atom.

Before we leave the hydrogen atom and go on to consider the hydrogen molecule, let's digress for just a moment to mention one further point. In Fig. 6.2, we saw that the largest number of atoms would be in the ground state, the next largest number in the first excited state, and so on. A mathematical relationship can be found between the number of atoms that are in various states. Rather than derive this relationship here, however, we will simply give the result. If we say that n_i is the number of atoms in state i, n_j the number in state j, and that E_i and E_j are the respective energies, we find that

$$\frac{n_i}{n_j} = e^{-(E_i - E_j)/kT}, \qquad (6.1)$$

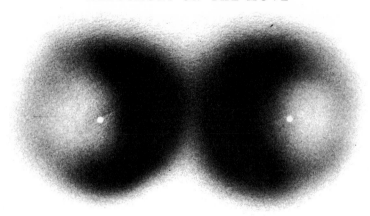

Figure 6.3

where k is the Boltzmann constant (equal to 1.385×10^{-18} erg/deg) and T is the absolute temperature. As we go along we will find that it is sometimes helpful to express our ideas not only verbally but mathematically with relationships of this form.

We still have in mind that our original objective was to consider electrons in solids, although so far we have confined ourselves to the atoms in a container of hydrogen gas. Eventually we will reach the solid itself, but our next step toward this goal is to examine the molecule. The hydrogen molecule is composed of two hydrogen atoms, as shown in Fig. 6.3. The ground state is indicated by the dark areas, as it was in Fig. 6.1. We can see that the charge density is greatest in the region between the two nuclei (protons). The hydrogen molecule is exceedingly stable; it does not easily break up into two hydrogen atoms. The reason for this stability is that the two atoms share their electrons; the two electrons essentially form a "cement" between the two protons, binding the atoms together. We call this a *covalent bond*, meaning that each atom participating in the bond contributes one electron. Now, it is not hard to believe that removing one of these electrons would tend to weaken the bond; however, it may be surprising to learn that adding a third electron to the bond will not materially strengthen it. In other words, the two-electron, covalent bond is ideal. Without going into the reasons, which would involve a long digression into quantum mechanics, let's simply accept this as a fact.

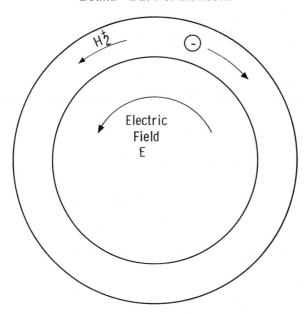

Figure 6.4

Just as there were excited states of the hydrogen atoms, so there are excited states of the hydrogen molecules. Furthermore, just as we were able to free an electron from the hydrogen nucleus (ionization), we are also able to free an electron from the hydrogen molecule. Again this is referred to as ionization, and the properties of the excited levels will also follow a mathematical law, such as Eq. 6.1.

What happens if we apply a constant electric field to a container of hydrogen molecules? For simplicity, we will imagine that the container is shaped like a doughnut, as shown in Fig. 6.4. Let's assume that a constant electric field E, in the direction indicated, exists in the doughnut. What then happens qualitatively? The gas in the container is composed of molecules in the ground state and other molecules in various excited states. In addition, due to ionization we also have free electrons and hydrogen molecule ions. Now the constant electric field can exert a force only on a charged body. Clearly, the molecules in the ground state or excited states are neutral, and therefore unaffected by the field. However, the hydrogen molecule ions are accelerated in the direction of the electric field, and the electrons in turn are accelerated in the opposite direction. Therefore, we have a flow

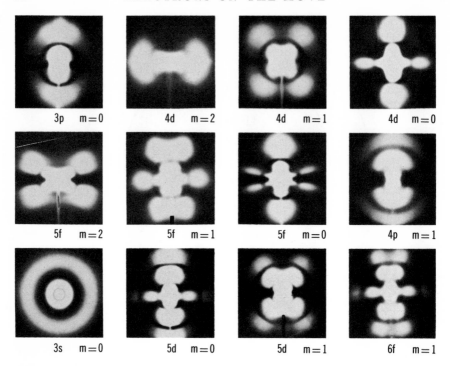

3p	m = 0	4d	m = 2	4d	m = 1	4d	m = 0
5f	m = 2	5f	m = 1	5f	m = 0	4p	m = 1
3s	m = 0	5d	m = 0	5d	m = 1	6f	m = 1

These diagrams indicate the distribution of the electron in a hydrogen atom; the nucleus, a single proton, is to be imagined at the center, and the relative brightness at any point in the surrounding figures is proportional to the probability of finding the electron at that point. The figures are cross sections of corresponding three-dimensional distributions, with a vertical axis of rotational symmetry in the plane of the figure. Each figure shows a different state of excitation of the atom, characterized

of electric charge, and thereby an electric current. Since the electric field gives a constant acceleration to the charged particles, what prevents them from reaching higher and higher velocities? Knowing that the current is proportional to the number of charges passing a given cross section in unit time, we might expect the current simply to increase continuously. However, there is an effect that tends to work against the electric field—the collisions between charged particles and neutral molecules. Eventually, of course, a balance will be struck between the effects of the electric field and the resistance effected by the collisions. When this happens, we reach a constant current.

Now let's suppose that in the absence of an electric field, the charged particles move in random directions; in other words, we have

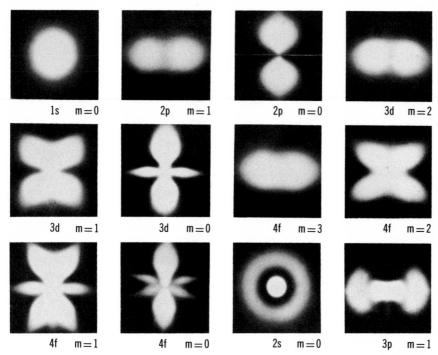

1s m=0	2p m=1	2p m=0	3d m=2
3d m=1	3d m=0	4f m=3	4f m=2
4f m=1	4f m=0	2s m=0	3p m=1

(Photographs from *Introduction to Atomic Spectra*, by Harvey E. White.
Copyright 1934. McGraw-Hill Book Company. Used by permission)

by the corresponding quantum numbers n, l, and m. These figures, which resemble what we might expect to see if we could view a hydrogen atom through an enormously (but impossibly) powerful microscope, are actually ingenious time-exposure photographs of a suitably shaped flat pattern, rotated during the exposure. For details, see H. E. White, *Physical Review*, Vol. 37, p. 1416 (1931).

the same number of particles moving in any given direction. Then let's assume that between collisions the charged particle behaves in the same way as the free particle we discussed in Chapter Four. We further assume that when a particle collides with another, it has an equal chance of being scattered or deflected in *any* direction. Our fourth assumption is that the electron suffers a collision every t_e seconds, and the hydrogen molecule ion collides every t_i seconds. This last assumption is obviously a gross oversimplification, for the times between collisions will certainly vary from very short to very long, and therefore we will use a sort of average in our calculations.

Suppose we follow a particular particle, beginning our observation immediately after a collision. This time (t) we will call zero, and we will say the particle's velocity is v_{oi}. The subscript o refers to the time directly after collision, and the i identifies the particle we are observing. Referring again to Chapter Four, we see that we can write

$$v_i = v_{oi} + at, \qquad (6.2)$$

where a is the acceleration, and we know that

$$a = \frac{eE}{m}, \qquad (6.3)$$

if e is the electronic charge, E the electric field, and m the mass of the charged particle. If we let t designate the time between collisions, we may then write the *average velocity* of the ith particle during that time as

$$\bar{v}_i = v_{oi} + \frac{eE}{m}\frac{t}{2}. \qquad (6.4)$$

At each collision, this i^{th} particle obtains a new velocity v_{oi}; however, between collisions we find it has an average velocity $\dfrac{eE}{m}\dfrac{t}{2}$ in the direction of the field. If we follow this particle through a sufficient number of collisions, we know from our third assumption that v_{oi} will assume all possible directions. This means that the random motion of the charged particle, as it undergoes collisions in an electric field, has the overall result of giving the charge an additional velocity of $\dfrac{eE}{m}\dfrac{t}{2}$ in the direction of the field.

Looking again at our doughnut-shaped container of hydrogen gas, we see now that we can describe it by saying: If N is the number of ionized hydrogen molecules per unit volume, we must have N electrons per unit volume traveling in a direction *opposite* to the field with a velocity $\dfrac{eE}{m}\dfrac{t_e}{2}$ (where m is the electron mass), and N ionized molecules per unit volume traveling in the direction of the field with a velocity $\dfrac{eE}{M}\dfrac{t_i}{2}$ (where M is the mass of the ion). We are now ready to calculate the current in the doughnut by using Fig. 6.5. The current is simply the amount of charge passing unit area in one second. Since the electrons have an average velocity v_e, all electrons in the shaded area, shown at the left, will pass the dotted line to the cross-hatched section in one second. Similarly, the ions will pass this same

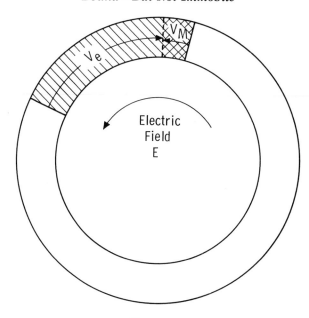

Figure 6.5

line from the cross-hatched section to the shaded area. Thus, the current density J (the current per unit area) may be written:

$$J = \frac{Ne^2Et_e}{2m} + \frac{Ne^2Et_M}{2M} = \frac{Ne^2E}{2}\left\{\frac{t_e}{m} + \frac{t_i}{M}\right\}. \qquad (6.5)$$

We know all the quantities in this equation except t, the time between collisions. To estimate this time, we consider the relative number of ionized molecules to be so small that the scattering of electrons and ions is done only by *neutral* molecules.

Before going on with these calculations, it will be helpful to mention the Equipartition Theorem, which states that at equilibrium all particles, regardless of their mass, have the same average kinetic energy; this kinetic energy is directly proportional to the absolute temperature. Expressed mathematically, this reads:

$$\tfrac{1}{2}mv^2 = \frac{\alpha}{2}kT, \qquad (6.6)$$

where k is the Boltzmann constant, and α is equal to the number of *degrees of freedom* of the particle; that is, the number of independent types of motion the particle may have. Without going into further detail at this point, let's simply say that $\frac{\alpha}{2} = 1$.

Since the total mass of the two protons of a molecule is some 2000 times greater than that of one electron, we realize that the molecules must be traveling much more slowly than the electrons. Therefore, we might say that the electrons are essentially moving through a cloud of stationary molecules. On the other hand, *if* we happened to be sitting on one of the electrons, we would be unable to tell whether we were at rest or in motion with respect to the molecules. In other words, we can take the point of view that the electrons are at rest, and that all the molecules are moving toward them in parallel paths with a speed equal to that of the electrons. Now, suppose that as a molecule collides with an electron, it is scattered out of the collection of molecules moving toward the electron. Our problem is to find out how many particles are so removed in one second. Whatever the number, its reciprocal will be the average time t between collisions.

If we say that the radius of the hydrogen molecule is R_M, and the radius of the particle to be scattered (either an electron or an ion) is R_x, we will see that the number scattered is simply equal to the number of molecules in a volume whose radius is $R_M + R_x$, and whose length is equal to the distance the electrons would travel in one second. (This is actually the *velocity*.) For if we assume that the radius of the electron is R_e, and the molecule has a radius R_M, it is obvious that when the two particles come closer together than $R_e + R_M$ there will certainly be a collision. Now, taking n as the number of neutral molecules per unit volume and n_s as the total number scattered, we find that

$$n_s = n\pi (R_x + R_M)^2\, v_x. \tag{6.7}$$

If t_e is the mean time of collision for an electron, then

$$t_e = \frac{1}{n_s} = \frac{1}{n\pi\,(R_e + R_M)^2\, v_e}, \tag{6.8}$$

where R_x has been set equal to R_e. Actually, since R_e is much less than R_M, we will neglect R_e in this expression. With this same expression, we can calculate the t for the hydrogen molecule ions by using v_M instead of v_e, and R_M instead of R_e. (The ion is essentially the same size as the molecule.) If we use the three equations, 6.4, 6.6, and 6.8, we now find that the current J may be expressed

$$J = \frac{Ne^2E}{2} \frac{1}{\sqrt{2kT}\, n\pi R_M^2} \left(\frac{1}{\sqrt{m}} + \frac{1}{4\sqrt{M}} \right). \qquad (6.9)$$

The mass of the electron is m and the mass of the molecule (or the molecule ion) is M.

Before discussing this equation, we must first say something about N, the number of ionized molecules per unit volume. We already know, from our previous discussion, that this quantity is dependent on the temperature. It can be shown that as long as the number of ionized molecules is small compared to the total, the number N can be written

$$N = ne^{-E_o/2kT}, \qquad (6.10)$$

where E_o is the minimum energy required to remove the electrons. Since the electrical conductivity σ is defined as J/E, we arrive at the desired result:

$$\sigma = \frac{e^2}{2\pi R_M^2} \frac{e^{-E_o/2kT}}{\sqrt{2kT}} \left\{ \frac{1}{\sqrt{m}} + \frac{1}{4\sqrt{M}} \right\}. \qquad (6.11)$$

What does this mean? First, let's examine the temperature dependence of σ. We see that if $E_o/2kT$ is large, the numerator will increase more rapidly than the denominator. Thus, the conductivity will increase with increasing temperature. This is the case for insulators or semiconductors. On the other hand, in a metal E_o is actually equal to zero, and we see that in this case the conductivity will decrease with increasing temperature. We must remember that the exponential term arises because of an increase in the number of charge carriers as the temperature is increased. We see then that large numbers of additional carriers are produced in an insulator and that the number is relatively constant for a metal.

There is also another important point. In an ionized gas, there are two types of charge carriers: electrons and "defective bonds." It will become apparent later why we prefer this term, instead of calling them hydrogen molecule ions. One electron has been removed from the strong covalent bond, and this gives the complex a charge of $+1$. We will see that semiconductors have analogous methods of carrying current.

SOLIDS

With this background, we are now ready to tackle solids. We will start with diamond, crystalline carbon, and Fig. 6.6 shows its structure. We notice that each carbon atom has four other carbon atoms as its nearest neighbors. These neighbors form the corners of a regular tetrahedron, a very stable structure; in fact, it is one of the most stable.

Will our understanding of the hydrogen molecule and its covalent bond help us to understand the stability of this carbon structure? In the case of hydrogen, we saw that an exceptionally strong bond could be formed when each of the two hydrogen atoms contributed one electron to the bond. In the case of carbon, we find that four electrons surround the nucleus. The two innermost electrons, however, are too tightly bound to the nucleus to contribute to the bonding, and so we will ignore them. This leaves the possibility of forming *four* covalent bonds between *four* neighboring atoms. It is not very easy to visualize this in three dimensions, but the two-

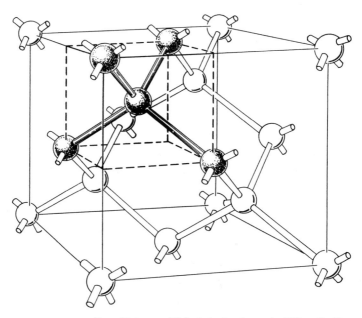

(From *Electrons and Holes in Semiconductors*, by William Shockley. Copyright 1950, D. Van Nostrand Company, Inc., Princeton, New Jersey)

Figure 6.6

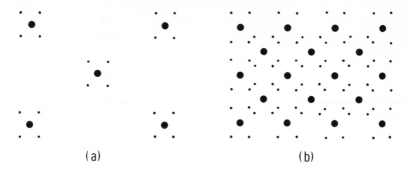

(a) (b)

Figure 6.7

dimensional model in Fig. 6.7 will help to show how this bonding comes about. In Fig. 6.7a, we see a lattice of carbon atoms, well
separated from one another. We have intentionally taken atoms far
enough removed from each other so that there is essentially no
interaction between them. If we were to move the atoms close
together, however, we would have the situation shown in Fig. 6.7b.
Here we see that each carbon atom has made four covalent bonds,
one with each neighbor. As might be expected, the result forms
an exceedingly stable structure.

Visualizing this basic structure in three dimensions, we see that
each atom is covalently bonded to four equidistant neighboring atoms
of the same type. This is true of all atoms in the lattice. Such
an arrangement, in which the atomic pattern is repeated regularly
throughout the solid, is called a *single crystal*. For our present
purposes it will be convenient to imagine the two-dimensional lattice
shown in Fig. 6.7b, although we must bear in mind that we are
actually dealing with the more complex structure of Fig. 6.6.

Now let's treat this lattice as if it were a huge molecule. As such, it
must have a ground state and a number of excited states. What corresponds to the ground state, and what to the excited state? It seems
reasonable to take the situation in Fig. 6.7b as the ground state, since
in this case all the bonds are complete. Suppose we now "ionize" a
bond; that is, we take an electron from one of the covalent bonds
and place it somewhere else in the lattice. This would produce
the situation shown in Fig. 6.8. Thus, if an electron is to be freed from
a bond, it must have energy at least equal to the ionization energy. If
energy in excess of the ionization energy is given, the free electron,

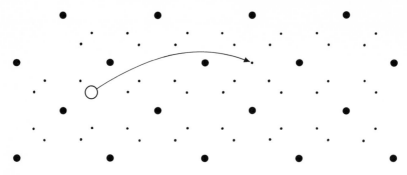

Figure 6.8

usually called a *conduction* electron, will also have some kinetic energy. The site in the covalent bond from which the electron is missing is called a *hole*, for obvious reasons.

How many conduction electrons will there be at any given temperature? As we might expect, at $0°K$, we find the ground state of the solid; that is, all covalent bonds are complete and there are no electrons or holes. (In a pure crystal, the number of electrons and holes must always be equal.) As the temperature is increased, the solid acquires energy, part of which goes into breaking up bonds. The higher the temperature, the more broken bonds and the more electron-hole pairs. The derivation of the exact mathematical expression for the number of conduction electrons is rather involved, and it it not necessary to give it here. However, the form of the dependence is analogous to the case of the ionized hydrogen molecule. The number of conduction electrons per cm^3, n_c, is given by

$$n_c = Ne^{-E_i/2kT}, \qquad (6.12)$$

where N is related to the number of levels per cm^3 available to the electron and the hole. (This number is normally about 10^{20}.) E_i is the *ionization potential*.

In order to give this expression some "life," let's examine a typical case to determine the number of conduction electrons at several temperatures. In a solid, a typical value for the ionization potential E_i might be several tenths of a volt or of the order of $2000 k$ (where k is again the Boltzmann constant). If we say that $N = 10^{20}$, we can construct a table giving the relationship between temperature T and the number of conduction electrons n_c per cubic centimeter.

TABLE 6A

T	n_c (number/cc)
$0°$K	0
$50°$K	2×10^{11}
$100°$K	5×10^{15}
$200°$K	6×10^{17}
$500°$K	1.2×10^{19}

Just as we expected, there are no free charge carriers at $0°$K. But at $50°$K there already appears to be an immense number. It is necessary to view this number in the proper perspective, however. In a cubic centimeter of a crystal,, there are approximately 10^{22} bonds. Since there are 10^{11} conduction electrons, there must be 10^{11} broken bonds. This means that only one bond in 10^{11}, one in a hundred billion, is broken at $50°$K. Nevertheless, we see that by the time we reach $500°$K, one bond in every 700 is broken. It becomes obvious that the fraction of broken bonds varies with astonishing rapidity as the temperature varies.

What happens when we apply an electric field to the solid? We saw in the case of a gas composed of hydrogen molecules that the ionized electrons moved in one direction, and the broken bonds (the molecule ion) moved in the opposite direction. Is there an analogy in the case of the solid? First, let's consider the conduction electrons. Once the electron is removed from its bond, it is free to wander through the lattice. When an electric field is applied, the motion will naturally tend to be directed. As it moves through the lattice, the electron frequently collides with the atoms that form the lattice. This is analogous to the electron in the hydrogen gas being scattered by the molecules. If we were to watch an electron long enough, and measure the time between each collision, we could finally determine the average time t_e between collisions.

Now let's examine the situation with the holes. The very nature of the solid prevents the bonds from moving in exactly the same way they do in the hydrogen gas, but there is a very close similarity. If we study Fig. 6.9, we see that the broken bond, or hole, at point (a) can move to point (b) simply by having an electron move from the bond at point (b) to the bond at point (a). In other words, when an electron moves from bond to bond in a solid, it leaves a hole behind

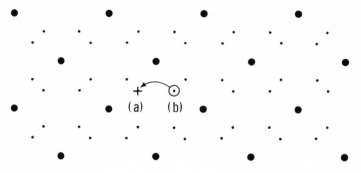

Figure 6.9

in the broken bond and annihilates the hole in the next bond it joins. Therefore, we can say that the holes, or broken bonds, move in a direction opposite that of the electron. And this is precisely the way physicists speak of the process. Instead of saying that the electron moves from bond to bond, they prefer to say that the *hole* moves from bond to bond. To make it easier to discuss its motion in a direction opposite to the electric field, we treat the hole as if it had a positive charge equal and opposite to that of the electron. It turns out that the hole, when properly treated, obeys equations very similar to those applying to electrons. This is why in modern physics the hole has been elevated to the full status of a particle. As such, it must have a charge, an average time between collisions, and a mass. We have already discussed the charge, and the average time between the collision of holes is analogous to that between the collision of electrons. However, the mass may present a problem to anyone unfamiliar with modern physics.

Before discussing the mass of these particles, we should mention one more point regarding the creation of electrons and holes as the temperature is increased. First, let's write a sort of chemical equation for the formation of a hole and an electron. Remember, bound electrons do not count.

NOTHING $\leftrightharpoons$ HOLE + ELECTRON

In other words, starting with nothing—no hole, no electron—we may create both an electron and a hole simply by removing an electron from a bond. As with all chemical equations, the one we have written indicates that the reverse reaction must also be able to take place.

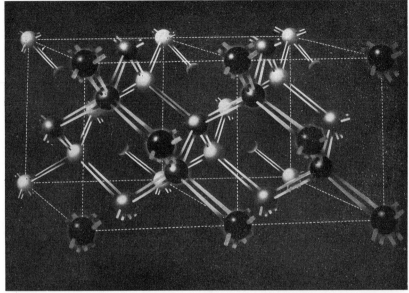

(a)

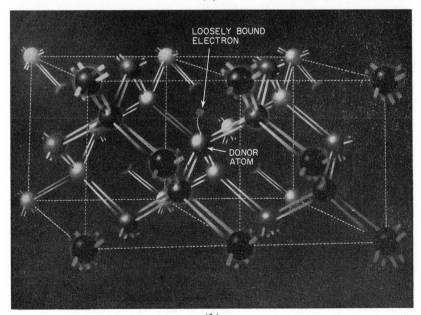

LOOSELY BOUND
ELECTRON

DONOR
ATOM

(b)

In this group of six photographs, A is a representation of a pure and perfect germanium or silicon lattice, showing the covalent electron bonds as double lines. In B, a pentavalent donor atom (1) has been substituted for a normal lattice atom; note the loosely bound fifth electron just above it. In C, this fifth electron (2) has

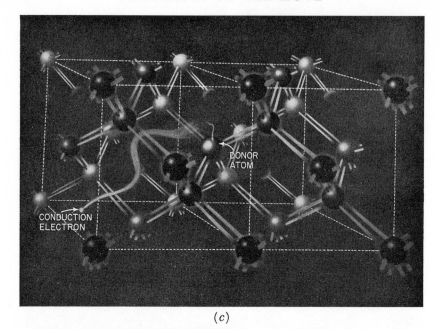

(*c*)

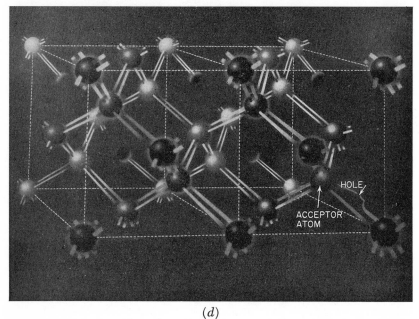

(*d*)

been broken away from the donor, or ionized, by thermal agitation, and is available
to carry an electric current. D shows a trivalent acceptor atom (3) substituted into a
lattice site; note the incomplete bond (4). E shows how this bond can be completed
at the expense of an electron (5) from a nearby bond (in this figure, however, still to

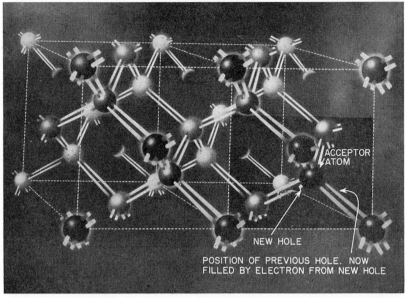

(*e*)

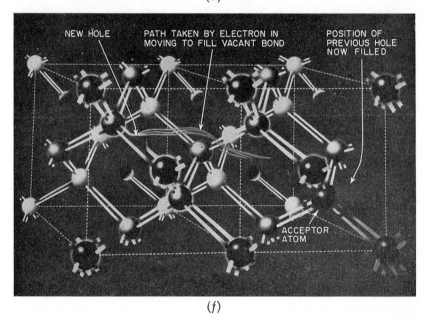

(*f*)

(Photographs from *The ABC's of Germanium,* by J. P. Jordan.
Electrical Engineering, July, 1952. Used by permission)

the acceptor), thus changing the position of the broken bond (4). F shows the broken bond, or hole, migrating through the lattice as a current carrier, by successive excitation of electrons from bond to bond.

This is indeed the case. It is quite possible for an electron to get to a point in the lattice structure close enough to a hole to essentially "fall" into it. This raises an interesting question. Do the concentrations of holes and electrons change rapidly in time? If the solid is at a constant temperature, the answer is no. Let's see why this is so. We mentioned earlier in our discussion that energy is required to create an electron and a hole; that is, the electron must somehow be given enough energy to be ionized. By the same token, when an electron drops into a hole, it must give up the exact amount of energy it has acquired, because otherwise the law of conservation of energy would be violated. It can be shown that when an electron recombines with a hole, the energy it gives up passes along through the solid, causing another electron to break its bond at some other point, and thus create another hole. Therefore, when we give the numbers of conduction electrons, as we did in Table 6A, we must not overlook the fact that we are dealing with a *dynamic* equilibrium, rather than a *static* one. This means that although we are able to state that the number of conduction electrons will be 10^{15} at $100°K$, we are obviously aware that it will not always be the *same* 10^{15} electrons.

Returning to the question of the mass of electrons and holes, it may seem obvious that the electron mass is equal to its weight of 9×10^{-28} grams, and that the hole weighs nothing and has no mass, since after all it isn't anything. Of course, it must be clear that there is something wrong with this reasoning, because otherwise we would not be making such a point of it. Let's go back for a moment to the meaning of the word "mass" as we considered it in connection with hydrogen gas. We said, in this case, that the only force acting on the charged particles was the external electric field. This allowed us to calculate the acceleration of the particle by using Newton's law, $F = ma$. Here F is equal to eE (E is the external electric field) and m is the mass of the charge. But we must remember that this equation gives the acceleration of a particle of mass m only if the force F includes *all* the forces acting on the particle. Have we taken care of this point in the case of the hydrogen gas? Have we, indeed, considered all the forces which act on the charged particle between collisions? Clearly, we have not, because we have neglected the fact that the other charges in the gas produce an electric field which acts on the particle in question. However, in the case of a gas, the net result of these forces is small compared to the applied electric field, and normally they may be neglected. *On the other hand,* in the solid this is not necessarily the case. In the solid, the conduction electrons are at all times close to the atoms of the solid. These atoms exert strong forces on the conduction electrons. By the same token, strong forces are also exerted on the holes; that is, the electrons that cooperate to give the holes a net motion have strong forces exerted on them. In fact, since these electrons in general are closer to the nucleus, they should be more strongly affected than others. This means that when we write Newton's law in the form $F = ma$ for the conduction electrons, we must include in F not only the external electric field, but also the forces exerted on the electrons by the charges in the solid itself.

For this reason, it might appear that our analogy with gases will not bear fruit. However, it turns out that we can take account of all the other forces by a simple but correct artifice. Instead of writing $F = ma$, where F is the *total* force on the electron, and m is the mass of the electron, we write

$$F = eE = m^*a, \qquad (6.13)$$

where m^* is called the *effective mass.* Comparing this equation carefully with $F = ma$, we see that the total force has been replaced by only the external electric field, and the electron mass has been replaced by something we call the *effective* mass. The acceleration is the same in both equations. Now, we find that Eq. 6.13 is much more pleasant to work with than $F = ma$, because it allows most of the formalism of the gas problem to be carried over into solids. However, have we really accomplished anything? In $F = ma$ we had the problem of determining the forces exerted by the atom of a solid on the conduction electrons. This is an exceedingly difficult problem. In Eq. 4.13 we have to calculate the effective mass m^*, which obviously must be the same problem—and therefore no easier. However, the idea of effective mass is a very convenient one, and as we go along we will get a better "feel" for this quantity. It should be pointed out now that an equation similar to 4.13 can be written for holes, and thus we speak of the effective mass of both electrons and holes.

To investigate the electrical conductivity of the solid, we will use the results of our calculation in gas, and write

$$\sigma = \frac{ne^2}{2} \left\{ \frac{t_{holes}}{m^*_{holes}} + \frac{t_{electrons}}{m^*_{electrons}} \right\},$$

remembering that t is the average time between collisions and n is the number of electrons and holes. In the case of a gas, the ions contributed only a small fraction to the total conductivity; however, in the case of solids, it is often found that the effective masses of electrons and holes are comparable, and essentially both contribute to the conductivity.

It is very important to understand that in the solids we are discussing there are *two* sources of current carriers: holes and electrons. Sometimes this is a little hard to swallow, because after all the motion of holes is nothing more than the motion of electrons in the opposite direction. This is a valid argument, but we must realize that the electrons that aid the motion of the holes differ in behavior from the conduction electrons. The conduction electrons are the *ionized* electrons; those contributing to hole motion are electrons in the covalent bonds. Thus, a difference in behavior is to be expected. It would be quite correct to speak of conduction electrons and bond electrons, instead of electrons and holes. However, the latter terms are commonly used.

We have based our discussion of solids on a crystal of pure diamond—carbon—but it should be pointed out that the same ideas apply to any pure crystal in which the atoms are held together by covalent bonds.

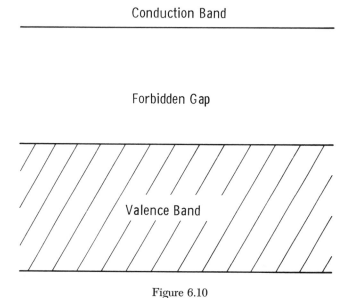

Figure 6.10

We can graphically summarize our description of the solid with Fig. 6.10. Electrons in the covalent bond have a range of energies within the *valence band,* as shown. Above this region is the *forbidden gap,* or *forbidden band,* in which no electrons are found. This band extends until we reach the ionization potential of the solid, and above this point the electrons take on kinetic energy; the conduction electrons occupy the region called the *conduction band.*

IMPURITIES IN SOLIDS

What happens when impurities are added to a pure crystal? The answer to this question applies to all semiconductors, which will be discussed in detail in the next two chapters. At present we will deal specifically with germanium, Ge, for the sake of clarity.

Let's first re-examine the lattice structure shown in Fig. 6.6, since germanium crystallizes in this same lattice. We see that each atom contributes four electrons to the bonds, but suppose one germanium atom were removed and replaced by a phosphorous atom. (Such a structure is still called a single crystal, even though it does not consist of a repetition of identical units.) Phosphorous is *pentavalent,* which means that it has *five* electrons to contribute to the bonding. Since only four electrons are needed for the germanium bond, this leaves one phosphorous electron with nothing to do. The situation is illustrated in Fig. 6.11. As we have already mentioned, it takes a certain quantity of energy to ionize a bond; however, the extra phospho-

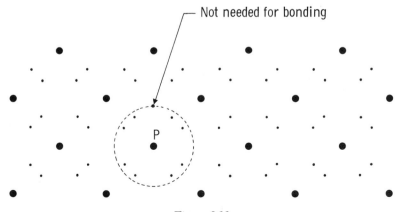

Figure 6.11

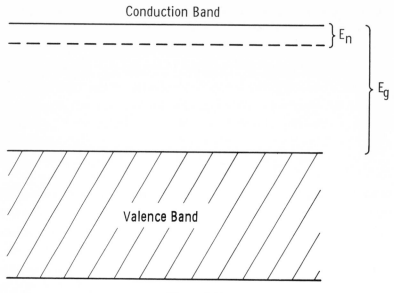

Figure 6.12

rous electron is not in the bond. Therefore, we might expect that this extra electron could be ionized somewhat more easily, and in fact this turns out to be the case, as shown in Fig. 6.12. An energy E_g is required to ionize an electron from a bond, thus giving an electron and a hole. But only an energy E_n is needed to ionize the fifth electron from an atom such as phosphorous. Just as we said before that the number of electron-hole pairs formed was proportional to $e^{-E_g/2kT}$, we can also show that the number of electrons produced from pentavalent impurity sites is proportional to $e^{-E_n/2kT}$. Since E_n is less than E_g, we see immediately that percentage-wise the impurity atoms are more highly ionized than the bonds.

Although we have been referring to a phosphorous impurity, it should be clear that any pentavalent impurity is satisfactory. In the case of germanium, for example, we find that phosphorous, arsenic, or antimony impurities are suitable to produce energy levels just under the conduction band. Such impurities add extra conduction electrons to the lattice and are therefore called *donors*. Since the sign of the charge of these electrons is negative, semiconductors containing these pentavalent impurities are said to be *N-type*. In addition to the electrons furnished by the impurities, there will also be present both electrons and holes produced, as in pure materials, by thermally broken bonds. The term N-type is usually reserved for materials in which the electron concentration due to the impurities is greater than that due to thermal generation. Since in the N-type material there are many more electrons than holes, electrons are called *majority carriers* and holes are known as *minority carriers.*

As we have said, germanium has four electrons to contribute to the bonding schemes; phosphorous has five. But suppose we introduce an atom that has only *three* electrons to contribute. It is obvious that such an impurity would result in one broken bond. Now, we saw that in pure materials a broken bond can move through the lattice by the simple expedient of having a neighbor bonding electron jump into the broken bond. The hole in pure germanium was equally satisfied at any point in the lattice; that is, there was no attraction to a particular point. But in the present case, there is a complication: the hole "prefers" to stay in the neighborhood of the *trivalent* atoms. The situation is similar to that of the electrons and the pentavalent atoms, which we discussed before.

Let's look again at Fig. 6.7b, and imagine removing an electron from one of the bonds. We realize, of course, that this situation cannot actually exist because the crystal is not electrically neutral. But one way to achieve electrical neutrality would be to remove a proton from one of the germanium atoms, which would effectively transmute the germanium atom into a *gallium* atom. What effect would this have on the hole? We want to show that if the hole had its own way, it would locate itself in a bond adjacent to the gallium atom. As we have said, the hole is simply the absence of an electron, and therefore it bears a positive charge with respect to the rest of the lattice. On the other hand, since the gallium has one less proton than the germanium, it "looks" negatively charged to the rest of the nuclei. Knowing that positive and negative charges attract one another, we can readily understand why the hole "prefers" to be neighbor to a gallium. An energy level diagram for this situation looks like Fig. 6.13, where the distance between the valence band and the impurity levels is labeled E_p. Contrary to the pentavalent situation, in the case of holes the impurity levels are unoccupied at $0°K$. That is, an electron does not occupy that state. Each impurity level in this case represents the vacant site in the broken bond adjacent to a

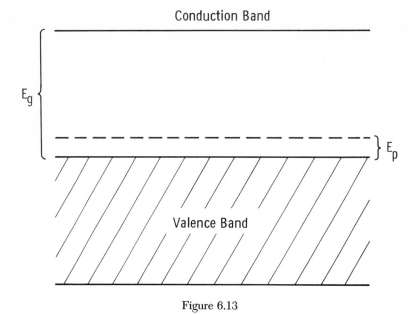

Figure 6.13

gallium, and this means that an electron from a neighboring bond can move into this level. However, it is obvious that the electron needs some additional energy (E_p) to make this move.

In contrast to the case of N-type material, trivalent impurities thus contribute extra holes to the lattice by absorbing electrons from the bonds. Such impurities are accordingly called *acceptors*. Since the charge of a hole is positive, material with trivalent impurities is called *P-type*, and in this case the majority carriers are holes and the minority carriers are electrons.

Before we go on to investigate the operation of some semiconductor devices, one final point should be made clear. In discussing the electrical conductivity of semiconductors, we must take into account both the holes *and* the electrons. Furthermore, the original source of the conduction electrons is immaterial. It makes no difference, for example, whether a conduction electron results from an electron being excited from the valence band into the conduction band, or if it arises from a pentavalent impurity site at the conduction band.

7

Travelers
at the Junction

TO UNDERSTAND the operation of semiconductor devices, we must first consider the behavior of an important basic structure, called the *P-N junction*. Rather loosely defined, this structure is the boundary between two adjacent regions of a single crystal. These two regions differ in their impurity content, by which one region is made N-type, the other P-type. Such a junction is important for two reasons. First, it functions as a *rectifier*, an electrical one-way valve which permits current to flow across the junction more easily in one direction than in the other. This action is essential in transforming electric current from alternating to direct, and also for signal detection in radio reception. Second, a flow of current increases the minority carrier concentration on either or both sides of the junction well above its equilibrium value. This process, called *injection*, is fundamental in the operation of the junction transistor, as well as many other semiconductor devices.

In our discussion, we will define a junction as the boundary region between two semiconductors of opposite type, as already described; a junction rectifier, or junction *diode*, will designate a complete structure or device, comprising the junction itself, with its N and P regions on either side, as well as the metallic contacts to these regions made at some distance from the junction by soldering or some similar process. These contacts allow external voltages to be impressed on the junction.

Using a rather idealized model, let's first examine the distribution of charges and potential when no external voltage is applied to the junction. We will then go on to consider the effect of disturbing these conditions by applying an external voltage, observing the current that flows as a result of this unbalance. Later we will similarly examine the operation of a junction transistor.

JUNCTIONS WITH NO APPLIED VOLTAGE

Let's assume that in our model of a junction the N and P regions initially are entirely separated physically and isolated from each other. Imagine that each is itself in internal equilibrium, as described in preceding chapters, and that these two separate regions are subsequently brought into intimate physical contact. Solely as a result of this contact, a redistribution of charge and potential occurs. In actual fact, however, a practical junction cannot be made in this manner, since it is impossible to achieve the necessary perfection and continuity of crystal structure at the junction because of inevitable surface roughness and layers of contaminants. It is likewise impossible to obtain sufficiently precise alignment. In practice, junctions are formed within the body of a single crystal block of material by processes which do not disrupt the crystal structure, for example, by diffusion of impurities into the material.

Let's imagine, however, that we are able to surmount these limitations of technique, and form a junction by this highly idealized process. Such an imaginary procedure, conceivable in principle but impossible in practice, is often referred to by physicists as a "gedanken experiment," *gedanken* being German for "imaginary" or "contemplated."

First, consider the N block, in which there is a uniform distribution of donor atoms, fixed in the parent crystal lattice. Let's assume that each of the donor atoms is ionized, which is true of germanium at room temperature, for example, and that the electrons thereby freed from the donors are uniformly distributed throughout the block. The word "uniform" must be understood here in the sense of the average distribution over a volume large compared with atomic dimensions, that is, a volume containing at least several thousand atoms, but nevertheless very small compared with the size of the whole block. In this sense, uniformity implies that any two such equal volumes of the crystal block will contain very nearly equal numbers of electrons and donors, no matter where in the crystal these volumes are chosen. Each such volume is thus electrically neutral, consisting as it does of neutral atoms of the parent crystal, plus equal numbers of electrons and positive donor ions (as well as much smaller equal numbers of thermally generated electrons and holes). Unlike the donor ions, the electrons are not fixed, but are free to move about through the lattice. We can think of them as drifting in a rapid, random manner somewhat reminiscent of the erratic darting of a swarm of bees. There is a restriction on this motion, however. If the distribution of charge is to be uniform, any flow of electrons into a not-too-small volume must be accompanied by an equal flow out of the volume.

Let's examine in detail this condition of uniform carrier distribution. We will see that this assumption is not arbitrary, but actually a natural consequence of diffusion and electrical effects. As we go along, we will also gain an understanding of the way in which these effects occur both singly and in combination.

Imagine a collection of identical small objects, so distributed in space that their x coordinates can have only integral values. We might think of such a collection as being similar to marbles on a washboard; the permitted integral values of the x coordinate perpendicular to the washboard's ridges and valleys would be those corresponding to the valleys, as shown in Fig. 7.1. Now, let's introduce some recurrent agitation, such as a repeated shaking of the washboard; perhaps striking it with a hammer. Let's assume that each disturbance will cause each object, or marble, to change its x coordinate by one unit, either increases or decreases being permitted; each marble will jump out of its groove, landing in an adjacent valley on one side or the other. This is a reasonably accurate though slightly idealized model of the process called *diffusion*.

Since the object, or marble, must surely go one way or the other, we can say that the probability P_r of a jump to the right plus the probability P_l of a jump to the left is equal to unity. Furthermore, if we

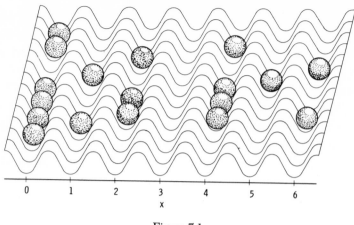

Figure 7.1

suppose that the nature of the disturbance makes it equally likely that the marble will move in *either* direction, it follows that P_r and P_l are each equal to one-half. In the case of the washboard, we might obtain such a symmetrical situation by carefully controlling the conditions, making the board absolutely level and striking it vertically upward from beneath. The same effect might actually be more easily achieved by flipping a coin for each marble and displacing the marble accordingly to right or left, repeating the process for each disturbance.

For the moment, let's suppose that $P_r = P_l = \frac{1}{2}$, and consider the rate at which marbles cross some specific ridge, such as that located at $x = 5\frac{1}{2}$, for example. At any given instant of disturbance, the number of marbles crossing to the right from $x = 5$ to $x = 6$ is on the average one-half the total number previously located in valley 5, and approaches almost exactly one-half as the number of marbles in question increases. The other half, of course, bounce into valley 4. Similarly, the number crossing to the left is one-half the number previously occupying valley 6. The total or net number crossing from left to right is then half the difference in the previous populations of valleys 5 and 6. A typical line graph of the population of all the valleys at some particular instant between disturbances is shown in Fig. 7.2. We see that at the next disturbance the net flow across any ridge will be proportional to the negative of the slope of the population graph at the coordinate of that ridge. Similarly, after a disturbance, the net increase in population of any given valley is equal to the net number coming into the valley from the left, minus the net number going out of the valley to the right. This increase is a measure of the rate of change of the valley's population and is proportional to the difference between the slopes of the population graph at the coordinates of the adjacent ridges.

This illustrates an important principle: The time rate at which material is transported by diffusion is proportional to the space rate of change of the material's concentration. *Time rate of change* means how greatly a quantity differs when compared at two successive times at the same point. Similarly, *space rate of change* means how greatly a quantity differs when compared at two adjacent points at the same time. This space rate of change, the slope of the population graph above, is called the *gradient,* and the ratio of the diffusive flux (rate of transport) to the gradient is called the *diffusion coefficient,* usually designated by D. The rate at which the material accumulates at a given point (corresponding to a valley in the washboard) under the influence of diffusion is proportional to the space rate of change of the gradient itself, or to the gradient of the gradient. Another important point about diffusion is that we do not need to think of the diffusing particles as repelling each other or affecting each other in any way. Even though the particle motions are entirely independent of each other, *net* motion from highly populated to sparsely populated regions occurs solely because there are more particles in the former

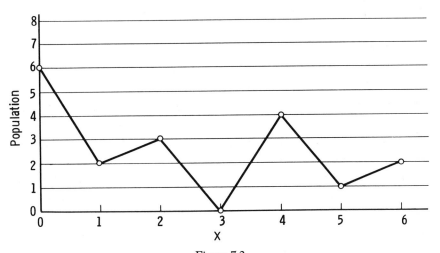

Figure 7.2

region which can migrate to the latter than vice versa. There is no "diffusive force" acting on the particles; indeed, the condition $P_r = P_l$ implies that any given particle is just as likely to migrate *against* the concentration gradient as with it.

The agitating influence we have assumed to recur corresponds physically to thermal agitation; the mobile carriers, or other particles, are in rapid random motion as a result of their thermal energy. Since this energy increases with rising temperature, the rapidity of diffusion also increases as temperature rises.

It is clear that diffusion is a process which tends to reduce any existing concentration gradients. For example, if at some instant a group of adjacent washboard valleys contains large equal numbers of marbles, while to the left another group is empty, a large slope in the population graph, or a large concentration gradient, exists at the ridge between these groups. When the next disturbance occurs, some marbles from the leftmost populated valley will be transferred to the rightmost empty valley, but not vice versa. This means that the population difference across the ridge, or the concentration gradient, will have decreased. Indeed, as we might suspect, if left to operate by itself diffusion will eventually erase all concentration gradients. As we mentioned before, the rate of concentration change is proportional to the gradient of the gradient of the concentration at that point. Hence, for the concentration to remain constant, or the rate of change to be zero, the gradient itself must be constant. We do not yet know what this constant value must be but, recalling that the rate at which material is transported by diffusion past a given point or through a given surface is proportional to the concentration gradient there, we conclude that at the outer surface of the region in question the gradient must be zero, if the region is not to gain or lose material continuously. Therefore, the gradient, being constant everywhere and zero at the boundaries, must be zero everywhere within the region, and hence the concentration must be constant. It is obvious that the effect of diffusion alone is enough to justify our original assumption of a uniform concentration of electrons within the N-type block of material. This assumption is consistent with the idea that the electrons are individually in rapid random motion, although this motion does not result in any *net* transport of charge, and therefore has no overall electric current associated with it.

We should also note that if the particles, or objects, are of two or more different kinds, the conclusions we have reached apply not only to the totality of particles, but to each of the individual sets of particles, as well. For example, if some of the marbles on our washboard had been chartreuse, some beige and some fuchsia, not only would the total transport rate of marbles have been proportional to the total marble concentration gradient, but the transport rate of any one color would have been proportional to the concentration gradient of the particular color. Diffusion of any one color would go on independently of diffusion of the other colors.

One further modification of our diffusion picture is useful. If we remove the restriction $P_r = P_l$ (while, of course, retaining the condition $P_r + P_l = 1$) by making $P_r = 0.51$, $P_l = 0.49$, for example, we observe that although jumps in either direction occur with *almost* equal frequency, there results a *net* motion of objects (or marbles, or electrons) to the right. In our washboard analogy such a change could be effected by tilting the board slightly to the right. In the case of the N-type semiconductor block, we could effect a similar result by applying an electric field, making the right-hand side of the block positive and the left-hand side negative. Electric current flow in a semiconductor, or for that matter in other material bodies, may therefore be considered a combination of the effects of diffusion and of electric field. The effect of the latter is to slightly unbalance the otherwise equal probabilities of leftward and rightward transitions. The important point to be observed here is that values of electric fields, normally thought of as large, actually cause only slight deviations of P_r and P_l from one-half. Therefore, we reach the somewhat astonishing conclusion that *the motion of individual charges in an electric current in a semiconductor is almost as likely to be against the field as with it.* (An important exception will be mentioned later.) The *net* motion, of course, is always in the direction of the field and is proportional to the degree of imbalance of the probabilities P_r and P_l, that is, it is proportional to the electric field. This latter statement is also true for the *average* motion of any individual carrier. The ratio of the average velocity of drift of a carrier to the magnitude of the electric field is called the *mobility* of the carrier, usually denoted by μ. For moderate electric fields this ratio is nearly independent of the field.

Now, let's reconsider our previous assumption that in diffusion the particles do not interact. In the case of electrons in a semiconductor such interactions certainly exist, since two electrons, being charges of like sign, will repel each other in accordance with Coulomb's law. We have already postulated that the donor ions are uniformly distributed and fixed in position. Since each excess conduction electron comes from a donor atom, the total number of donor ions and of excess electrons is equal; also equal are the much smaller numbers of electrons and holes produced by thermal breaking of bonds. If these electrons are distributed uniformly, any not-too-small volume of the N-type block will be electrically neutral, that is, it will contain negligible excess of either positive or negative charge. A deficiency of negative charge is electrically equivalent to an excess of positive charge, or vice versa. Since, as a whole, such a small volume has no charge, the electrons it contains will not appreciably affect the electrons in a similar volume nearby. If, however, the distribution of charge is not uniform, a region with a deficiency of electrons will have a net positive charge, while one with an excess of electrons will have a net negative charge. The electric field between these two regions, therefore, will cause a net electron flow from the excess region to the deficient region, until the charges are once again equalized, and the electric field reduced to zero. It is evident that the effects of both diffusion and electrical interaction are directed toward realizing a uniform distribution of charges. However, this is not contradictory to the well-known fact that in a conducting or semiconducting material these same electric effects force any *net excess* of mobile charge to reside on the *exterior* surfaces of the material. The preceding discussion, on the other hand, applies to that fraction of mobile charge (in this case, all of it) which is equal to the total charge of the fixed donor ions.

With this excursion into the philosophy of the effects of diffusion and electric fields, let's return now to our main theme—the *P-N* junction. Our assumption for N-type material, by now well-justified, was that the distribution of mobile electrons is uniform on the average. Adjacent to our N-type block we place a P-type block, which is to be regarded as an array of fixed negatively charged acceptor ions and an equal number of mobile holes. Both are uniformly distributed within an otherwise neutral parent semiconductor lattice, which by thermal excitation contributes much smaller equal numbers of mobile holes and electrons to the array. Now, let's imagine these two blocks brought into intimate contact, with the parent lattices joining so perfectly that no discontinuity exists. What, if anything, takes place?

We observe immediately that at the junction plane there is an enormous gradient in the concentrations of both holes and electrons. To the left of the junction, the electron concentration is a constant, equal to the original concentration in the N-type block. To the right, it is very small—zero, except for the few intrinsic electrons produced thermally in the P-type block. For holes, the reverse is true. Consequently, electrons will immediately begin to diffuse across the junction into the P-type material, while holes will simultaneously, but independently, diffuse into the N-type material.

If holes and electrons were uncharged and did not in any way interact, this process would proceed until the concentration of each particle was uniform throughout the entire combined volume of both materials. But as we shall see, this does not in fact happen. A hole from the P region, which diffuses across the junction, immediately finds itself amid a sea of hostile particles—the majority electrons of the N region—each hungrily waiting to recombine with the unwary hole, thus destroying both self and invader. The average length of time before the hole is annihilated, appropriately called the *lifetime* of the minority carrier, depends considerably on the crystal's perfection, as well as on several other factors. However, the lifetime usually ranges from a few microseconds to several hundred microseconds. During this time, the hole will diffuse into the N region a distance which may be some tenths of a millimeter, there finally recombining with an electron. A similar fate awaits the electrons, which initially diffuse from the N region into the P region.

It is undoubtedly apparent by now that this distance of some tenths of a millimeter is extremely large compared with the average spacing between majority carriers. In diffusing such a long distance, (and, incidentally, making several million collisions with the lattice of semiconductor atoms and impurities) the hole will certainly have had a great many close encounters with electrons. It would seem that the hole might have recombined with any one of these. How did it manage to avoid this fate for so long? The answer, which can be shown by a rather advanced mathematical treatment, is that the hole cannot recombine with just "any" electron which wanders nearby, but only with a neighboring electron having an energy and momentum related in a prescribed way to the energy and momentum of the hole. More specifically, energy and momentum must be conserved during the recombination. Furthermore, it turns out that these requirements normally cannot be satisfied in a region where the crystal lattice is perfect; some imperfection, such as an impurity atom or lattice defect, is required to absorb sufficient energy and momentum to conserve both these quantities. This explains why the lifetime is dependent on crystal perfection. The absorbed energy appears in the lattice as a small pulse of vibration, called a *phonon*, which is transmitted through the lattice by the forces between adjacent atoms.

This diffusive transfer of holes into the N region, and of electrons into the P region, results in an electrical charging of the two regions with respect to each other. The P region becomes negatively charged and the N region positively charged. In turn, this charge will produce an electric field between the two regions, that is, at and near the junction. Obviously, this field will oppose the diffusion process. As more and more charge is transferred by diffusion, the opposing field becomes stronger and stronger. It is intuitively evident (and also true, which is more than can be said of many things that are intuitively evident) that an equilibrium will be reached; no further net transport of charge across the junction will then occur.

What is the nature of this equilibrium? First, it should be pointed out that the term *equilibrium* may be applied to two rather different situations. The simpler of these is exemplified by the pendulum of a grandfather's clock, whose vacationing owner has forgotten to wind it; once the clock has run down, the pendulum simply hangs stationary at the lowest point of its arc, and there is no further motion apparent. This condition, called *static equilibrium*, is typified by a state of complete quiescence; the positions of all the bodies concerned (in this case, only the pendulum) can be accurately specified and are constant, that is, do not change with time. This description of equilibrium is usually accurate enough when all the objects concerned are relatively large, which generally includes objects visible to the naked eye. However, as the objects dwindle to microscopic size, the accuracy of such a description may decrease rapidly; it is rarely even approximately accurate if the objects are molecular in size, or smaller. This is because of the ever-present thermal agitation.

In situations involving very small objects, or very large numbers of objects, or both—which clearly is the case with the large numbers of electrons and holes near a junction, say 10^{14} per cubic centimeter—scientists usually abandon the search for an exact description of the system, which would require a precise determination of the coordinates or other properties of each object. Instead, we focus our attention on the problem of calculating a suitable *average* value for the desired quantities. Such an approach is preferable when the quantity whose average is to be calculated—for example, the number of molecules in a given subdivision of a larger volume of gas—fluctuates either with time or position, but approaches the calculated average more and more closely as the length of time, or the volume, over which the average is taken, increases. A situation in which this behavior occurs is called a *dynamic equilibrium.*

Some of the properties of a dynamic equilibrium may be illustrated by a slightly facetious example of a salesman's checking account balance. Without much imagination, we will call the salesman Mr. Smith. It is Mr. Smith's unfortunate fate to have a wife whose desires exceed her husband's means. The Smith's bank balance, torn between his dogged determination to avoid jail at the hands of his creditors, and his wife's ardent desire to outshine the neighboring Joneses, teeters precariously on the brink of insolvency. Occasionally, Mrs. Smith will deplete the budget by splurging at a department store, whereupon Mr. Smith is obliged to work evenings, earning extra commissions to restore the balance to the black; or perhaps occasionally he boosts the balance to an unusual height by landing a big sale, whereupon his wife restores it to its usual shabby state by buying that sofa she's had her eye on.

Here we see at work several elements of dynamic equilibrium. The quantity involved fluctuates as a result of two or more processes, not all tending to change it in the same direction. In this case, there are only two processes—his deposits and her withdrawals. The status of the account at any given time does not give much useful information about the Smith's financial stability, but the *average* balance over several months might well do so. This average will more and more nearly approach some constant value, assuming constancy of the Smith's living habits, as we increase the length of time over which the average is calculated. In like fashion, an instantaneous quantity in a system in dynamic equilibrium may vary with time, but its average over a given time interval will approach a meaningful constant, as the length of the interval becomes long enough. The question of how long is "long enough" is by no means trivial, but we will not attempt to answer it here.

By extending our analogy only slightly, we can illustrate another very useful way of calculating averages. If we assume Mr. Smith's many neighbors, including the Joneses, consist of husbands whose ambitions and earning capacities are similar, and whose wives' shopping preferences are also matched, little elasticity of imagination is required to conclude that the average balance of each family, as calculated above, should be much the same. Rather than average the balance of just one family over a long time, we can choose instead to observe at a given fixed time the balances of all the families, and average this quantity. If we suspect that the averages formed in these two quite different ways are in fact equal, we are right, provided the individual incomes and expenditures of each family are random in time and not affected by those of any other families. A little thought will show the last condition to be necessary. The equality of these averages demonstrates an extremely important principle: Many calculations of physics are founded on the plausible assumption that the value of some characteristic of a system in equilibrium, averaged over a long time, is equal to the value of the same characteristic of a large number of identical systems at a given time, averaged over all the systems. This is true whether the systems are isolated or interact randomly.

One final point must also be stressed. At least one of the processes affecting the quantity to be averaged must depend on the value of that quantity. In our example, both processes so depended: the lower the balance, the harder Smith labored to restore it; the higher it rose, the more freely his wife depleted it. It is not necessary that both or all processes be thus dependent. If Mr. Smith had worked for a fixed salary, presumably his wife would have limited her spending to suit their income, and equilibrium would again have been reached. We may reasonably argue, of course, that if her husband had received a raise, Mrs. Smith's spending would soon increase to match, and the balance would again stabilize, perhaps at a somewhat higher level. In these instances, only the rate of depletion depends on the balance, the accretion rate being fixed by other circumstances. But if none of the processes depends on the quantity in question, no equilibrium can occur; if Smith is on a fixed income and his wife shops without regard to the balance, stability can never result.

Strictly speaking, this discussion applies not only to equilibrium but to any *steady-state* process, loosely defined as one in which average conditions do not change with time. "Equilibrium" is a term usually reserved for those steady-state processes which have the additional property of no net energy transfers or conversions taking place. For example, flow of electricity in a wire can be a non-equilibrium, steady-state process, after the wire temperature has stabilized. It is steady-state, because the process variables—temperature, electron concentration, current, and potential distribution—do not change with time. However, it is not an equilibrium, because electrical energy is continuously converted into heat, which is then conducted or radiated away.

Let's see how this discussion is related to junctions. We are now aware that some dynamic equilibrium will be reached, that is, an actual distribution of charges, field, and potential will occur, fluctuating slightly and quite measurably with time, but remaining very close to an average distribution. The methods of calculating this distribution are illustrative of the general attack on many equilibrium problems. First, we *assume* that some arbitrary distribution or state of our system exists, and we ask, "Knowing the characteristics of the assumed distribution, can we predict how these characteristics will have changed, after a not-too-short time interval, as a result of the processes going on in the system?" Assuming an affirmative answer, we next ask, "Can we choose the initial arbitrary distribution in such a way that on the average the predicted changes are zero?" If we can do both, the distribution determined in this way obviously is an equilibrium. Mathematically, the first step usually requires the solution of a differential equation, a relation between rates of change of quantities, while the second requires fitting this solution to boundary values.

In applying this treatment to the *P-N* junction, the quantity whose distribution must be assumed is that of the mobile charges, the holes and electrons. Our choice of a trial distribution is not entirely pulled out of a hat, for we already have some idea how the charges must be distributed. For one thing, recombination will prevent the simultaneous occurrence of excess concentrations of both holes and electrons at the same place. Therefore, the carriers which diffuse across the junction, after the blocks are brought into contact, soon recombine with the local majority carriers of opposite sign. Since originally each block was electrically neutral, this annihilation of majority carriers will leave a layer of fixed, uncompensated, positive donor ions near the junction on the N side, and similarly a layer of fixed, uncompensated, negative acceptor ions on the P side. As used here, the term "uncompensated" means that the charge of these fixed ions is no longer matched by an equal and opposite average charge density of mobile carriers, so that each of these regions, on either side of the junction, contains a net fixed charge. The total uncompensated positive charge on the N side is exactly equal to the total uncompensated negative charge on the P side, so that the junction *as a whole* remains electrically neutral. However, the separation of this charge into adjacent layers of opposite type, a configuration called a *dipole layer*, results in an electric field in this region. As we remarked earlier, this is the field which precisely cancels the tendency for further net diffusive transport of electrons into the P region, or holes into the N region. Clearly its direction is proper for this result.

A dipole layer, as described above, does not result in any electric field outside the charged region. Hence, in the N and P regions outside the space-charge layers of the junction there will be no electric field, and no net flow of charge. Since these same conditions prevailed in these materials before the junction was formed, we conclude that joining the regions to form the junction has affected the charge configuration only in the immediate neighborhood of the junction. We now have a fairly detailed, though qualitative, picture of a junction, with an internal electric field which adjusts itself exactly to that value required to balance diffusive transport of mobile carriers. The junction dipole layer is bounded on either side by undisturbed N- and P-type regions respectively.

Since the electrons adjacent to the N side of the junction dipole layer have been assumed in thermal equilibrium, it follows that their velocities are random in direction and vary in magnitude about an average value. This turns out to be $\sqrt{3kT/m^*}$, roughly 10^7 cm/sec at room temperature. In this expression, T is absolute temperature, k is Boltzmann's constant, and m^* is the effective mass of the electron.

Since many electrons have velocities directed toward the junction, these enter the junction and penetrate some distance. Some are turned back, re-entering the N region, but in spite of the retarding effect of the electric field a few get through to the P region, where they become minority carriers. Conversely, minority electrons from the P region diffuse into the junction, and most of these, assisted by the field, migrate to the N region. Thus, there is a continual exchange of electrons between the N and P regions, yielding zero net flow, however. A similar statement applies for holes.

To make this picture quantitatively correct, let's try using our previous general principle again. If we assume a distribution of carriers, we then know where all the charges are and therefore can calculate the electric fields and the rate of diffusive transport. By a suitably judicious choice of the assumed distribution, we are able to make the net transport resulting from these two opposing effects be everywhere zero. This choice would then be the desired equilibrium distribution.

When we attempt to carry out this calculation, however, we observe at once that the distribution of charge carriers depends on the electric field, or electric potential, since the charges will tend to distribute themselves where their electrical potential energy is least. This effect is much like that of water in a lake, which distributes itself by flowing to the lowest places so that its gravitational potential energy is least. In turn, the electric field or potential depends on the distribution of charge carriers, since these charges, along with the fixed donor and acceptor ions, are actually responsible for the field. This interdependence of charge distribution and field means that our problem contains two unknown quantities, for which we must solve a pair of simultaneous equations. Of itself, this is no great obstacle, for it proves possible to eliminate one of these unknown quantities in a manner similar to that used for two linear algebraic equations in two unknowns, leading here to a single differential equation to be solved for the carrier distribution. However, it is found impossible to obtain a solution of this equation exactly, in terms of "simple" functions, such as trigonometric or Bessel functions. Being humanly lazy, physicists like when possible to work with such simple functions, whose properties are known and whose values are either tabulated or easily calculable. Therefore, the usual course of action is to look for sufficiently accurate *approximate* solutions of the equation, which *can* be expressed as combinations of simple functions. We will not burden ourselves here with the details of the solution. However, even those who have not yet mastered the mathematical tools necessary for the calculation should by now understand the philosophy of the method.

The results of such calculations show that extremely high electric fields, of the order of 10^4 to 10^6 volts/cm, are set up in the dipole region of the junction. As we might expect, this field is strongest precisely at the junction plane, decreasing almost exactly linearly with distance to zero at the outer edges of the charged layers. The total width of the charged region is small, about 10^{-4} to 10^{-6} cm, and the total potential difference across it—mathematically, the integral of the field over the junction—is roughly half a volt, depending on the impurity concentrations in the N and P regions. In most cases of physical interest, the junction field is sufficiently large that only a very small number of majority carriers on either side have high enough energy to penetrate far into the high-field region. Therefore, the field may be calculated fairly accurately by considering the junction to be entirely free of mobile carriers. (Such a calculation must be checked afterward for self-consistence, by seeing if the field computed in this way is actually large enough to justify the assumption of no mobile carriers in the junction.) This information may relieve anyone who has wondered why the fixed charges we have previously assumed to produce the junction field were not neutralized by majority carriers diffusing in from both sides. The answer, of course, is that almost all are kept out by the field. A few majority carriers from either side, which *do* have enough energy, penetrate into and perhaps cross the junction. Along with them are the minority carriers on either side, which diffuse into the high-field region and are then, for the most part, swept across by the field. All these constitute the charge-carrier traffic across the junction, to which we have referred before and whose net flow so far is zero.

Let's now summarize our picture of a junction. At equilibrium, with no external applied voltage, we find that on either side of the junction plane, the crystal is entirely depleted of mobile carriers. The fixed, ionized impurities in this *depletion layer* produce a rather high electric field, which prevents most of the majority carriers on either side from penetrating far into the junction. This field also results in a potential difference, roughly half a volt, between the regions on opposite sides of the depletion layer, the *N*-type side being positive with respect to the *P*-type side. The material outside the depletion layer is free of electric fields and has the same carrier concentrations it would have if no junction were present. Because of the combined effects of diffusion caused by the carrier concentration gradients and drift in the junction electric field, there is a continual exchange of both electrons and holes between the neutral regions bordering the junction. However, under the present conditions of no externally impressed voltage, the net flow of each type of carrier is zero.

When we first encounter this situation, we may wonder why this built-in potential difference cannot be made to furnish power to an external circuit. It seems that by connecting such a circuit across the terminals, which are attached to the *N* and *P* regions, respectively, we might create a perpetual motion machine. Why, in other words, can we not use a junction as a battery? The answer is that the act of attaching terminals to the *N* and *P* regions results in establishing *contact potentials* between these terminals and the semiconductor material of just such magnitude as to exactly cancel the effect of the junction potential in any external circuit. These potentials are set up by the interaction between the terminal material and the semiconductor in a fashion very similar to that which results in the junction potential. In fact, the junction potential itself may be considered a contact potential. No such external circuit can be made without this introduction of additional contact potentials. As long as the entire circuit is kept at uniform temperature, no current flow will result. However, this balance of potentials can be destroyed, for instance, by illuminating the junction from some external source such as sunlight. The light absorbed by the junction produces additional carriers (electrons and holes in equal numbers) which alter the junction potential, resulting in a net current flow in the external circuit. But, in this case, the junction is not being used as a battery; all the energy delivered to the external circuit comes from the light falling on the junction. Used in this fashion, a junction is popularly called a *solar cell.*

JUNCTION WITH EXTERNAL VOLTAGE APPLIED

Let's suppose the exact balance in the flow of each type of carrier in both directions across the junction is disturbed by applying to the junction terminals an external voltage, for example, from a battery. What happens? It seems likely that a net current will now flow, in a direction determined by the polarity of the applied voltage; of course, this direction must be the same as it would be if the junction were merely a resistor or a piece of wire. Otherwise, the junction would be acting as a source of energy, which is impossible. However, in sharp contrast to the case of the resistor, we might expect a striking change in the *magnitude* of the current, as well as a reversal of direction, when the polarity of the applied potential is reversed, its magnitude staying the same. With a resistor, no such difference is to be anticipated. A resistor, after all, is just a piece of wire, for example, which looks the same from either end; it is electrically symmetrical. We might say, on the other hand, a junction has a built-in sense of direction, determined by the direction of the electric field at the junction. We might expect the magnitude of the resulting current to depend on whether the fields produced by the battery aid or oppose the junction field. Let's see what we can deduce, either qualitatively or quantitatively, about the variation of current with applied voltage.

Taking first only the electrons, a common method of analyzing the current in a junction is to consider that all minority electrons, diffusing into the junction from the P side, are drawn across by the field to the N side. All the majority electrons of sufficiently high energy and suitably directed velocity, which enter the junction from the N side, will resolutely climb up the restraining electric-field barrier, emerging triumphant but exhausted, with about average thermal energy, on entering the P side. A similar picture is drawn for holes. It is then stated that for no applied voltage the total hole and electron currents are individually zero, these components cancelling in pairs; when an external voltage is applied, increasing or decreasing the junction field, these components no longer cancel, and the actual current flow is purportedly calculated by examining how each of these four components varies with the applied voltage. It should be pointed out that this kind of analysis requires the physical assumption that electrons which enter the junction from the N side can be distinguished during their entire crossing from those entering from the P side; otherwise, it is impossible to calculate the individual components. Except in the few cases where the mean free path, or average distance traveled between collisions, is so large that the electron is likely to traverse the entire junction without a collision, this assumption is quite unjustified; once an electron within the junction has undergone a collision or two, its energy and direction of motion have lost all relation to those it had on entering. In other words, we can no longer tell from which side of the junction the electron entered. The same conclusion, of course, applies to holes. Therefore, we must view as something of a fortunate coincidence the fact that such calculations yield results that agree reasonably well with experiment.

Although the results of this type of quantitative calculation are therefore questionable, it is true, nonetheless, that qualitatively speaking most of the minority electrons, diffusing into the junction from the P side, will be urged across the junction by the field, emerging at the N side as majority carriers; while only the more energetic of the majority electrons, diffusing into the junction from the N side, will have sufficient energy after many collisions to emerge at the P side as minority carriers. Most lower-energy electrons are reflected, so to speak, by the field and returned to the N region. Similar circumstances obtain for holes. From these considerations we can easily form a good qualitative image of the way in which the junction current varies with applied voltage. To do this, however, we must observe a fact which sounds reasonable, and can be justified mathematically, but which we will simply take here on faith: In an assembly of particles in thermal equilibrium, the relative fraction of these, which at any instant of time have energies equal to or greater than any given value E, decreases as E increases, and increases as the temperature T increases. For example, if we assume the density of the majority electrons in the N region is n per cubic centimeter, the number having thermal energies exceeding E (measured from the lowest energy possible for a conduction electron, which is the energy corresponding to the bottom of the conduction band) is very nearly

$$ne^{-E/kT},$$

decreasing exponentially as E increases.

Now, let's consider a situation wherein a voltage V is applied to the junction in such a manner that the N side is made more positive, the P side more negative. Since the internal electric field of the junction is already in this same direction, the applied potential results in strengthening this field and increasing the total potential, or energy difference, between the *N* and *P* regions. Because of this increase in the energy needed by a majority electron to cross the junction from the *N* region to the *P* region, fewer will have sufficient energy and the flow of electrons will drop very sharply as the voltage *V* rises. At

An electron beam microscope photographs a *P-N* junction, with and without bias. A sharply focused electron beam strikes the object being photographed, causing at the point of impact the emission of secondary electrons which are collected by a nearby electrode. As the electron beam is scanned across the object of study, the secondary emission current varies with the nature of the surface being scanned. This current, made to modulate the intensity of the electron beam in a synchronously scanned cathode ray tube, produces on the face of that tube an enlarged image of the object.

In photograph A, the two wires (less than half the diameter of a human hair) which are the leads to the junction are visible, their ends welded to the semiconductor. No

room temperature, the quantity kT is about $\frac{1}{40}$ of an electron volt; consequently, this electron flow will decrease by a factor of e for each $\frac{1}{40}$ volt of applied potential, and is therefore negligible when V is greater than about one-quarter volt.

(Photographs by Oliver Wells. Courtesy of Pulp and Paper Research Institute of Canada)

voltage is applied to the junction and thus the entire semiconductor is at a uniform potential; therefore, the collected secondary current is substantially constant over all the semiconductor's surface.

In photograph B, a reverse bias has been applied to the junction. This bias makes the N side of the junction sufficiently more positive than the P side that most of the secondaries emitted from the N region are now not collected. Thus the N region appears darker than the surrounding P region, clearly showing the convoluted shape of the junction.

On the other hand, the density of minority electrons in the *P* region is almost completely unaffected by the applied voltage *V*, as therefore is the rate at which they diffuse into the junction. Since practically all of the latter are carried across to the *N* side, whether or not *V* is applied, we find that the current which flows is very nearly independent of applied voltage in excess of a small fraction of one volt, on up to voltages of some hundreds of volts, where other processes occur. This direction of applied voltage, which aids the junction field, is called the *reverse* direction, and a junction with such a voltage applied is said to be *reverse biased*. The small voltage-independent current which flows, called the *reverse saturation current*, is carried at the junction entirely by minority electrons from the *P* region, and minority holes from the *N* region which behave in a fashion exactly analogous to that described above for electrons. The resulting currents are of the order of micro-amperes per square centimeter of junction area.

When, on the other hand, the applied voltage *V* opposes the internal junction field, the total potential difference between the two regions is reduced, causing a slight reduction in the minority carrier diffusion across the junction. This effect, however, is entirely insignificant compared with the effect on the majority carrier flow. The reason is that a reduction in the potential difference across the junction reduces the energy a majority carrier (electron in the *N* region or hole in the *P* region) must possess to have a reasonable chance of crossing the junction. As we have seen, the number having the necessary minimum energy increases exponentially as the required energy decreases. In consequence, when the applied voltage *V* opposes the internal junction field, then said to be in the *forward* direction, the current increases very rapidly as *V* rises, going to values of hundreds of amperes per square centimeter of junction area for applied voltages of some tenths of a volt. This case is just the opposite of that of the reverse current; the current at the junction is almost entirely composed of majority carriers from both regions, which of course become minority carriers on crossing the junction.

In this way we arrive at a qualitative idea of the variation of junction current *I* with applied voltage *V* similar to that sketched in Fig. 7.3. This asymmetrical behavior, called *rectification*, is of fundamental importance in many circuit applications, as mentioned earlier.

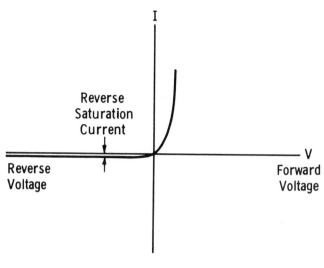

Figure 7.3

The high asymmetry exhibited by the curve (Fig. 7.3) suggests that for many purposes a junction might be approximated as a switch, closed when the applied voltage is in the forward direction, open when reverse voltage is applied.

To construct a quantitatively accurate picture of the action at a junction, it is necessary to be able to describe, in a precise mathematical way, the relationship between current flow and electric field in the semiconductor material. For regions outside the junction depletion layer, this can be done fairly well, the treatment being carried out by an extension of the previous discussion concerning the combined effects of diffusion and electric field, in which it was pointed out that the effect of an electric field can be included by slightly altering the probabilities P_r and P_l from one-half. In the depletion-layer region, however, the fields are much too high for this kind of treatment to be valid. Indeed, there exists today no adequate theory of the behavior of mobile carriers in such a high field region. The problem of filling this gap in our knowledge stands as a challenge to the imagination and ingenuity.

Lacking such a treatment at present, we must try to find some reasonable assumption with which to replace a better description; later the results must be subjected to experimental test. The assumption usually made is that, even when net current is flowing, the densities of minority and majority electrons on opposite sides of the junction are in thermal equilibrium (and similarly for holes), in spite of the fact that current flow is accompanied by energy dissipation, and hence one of our earlier requirements for equilibrium is violated. To simplify the calculations, usually the further assumption is made that outside the depletion region, the material is everywhere electrically neutral. Since the resulting current flow requires a finite, though small, electric field in these *quasi-neutral* regions, which in turn requires some excess of charge, this assumption of charge neutrality cannot ever be exactly correct. However, if the deviations from strict neutrality are small, as is usually the case, the assumption is close enough. With these and other reasonable assumptions, we can calculate the way in which current should vary with voltage. After we have looked more closely at the distribution of carriers when current is flowing, we will carry out this calculation in detail.

It was stated earlier that application of an external voltage to a junction affects the current flow by increasing or decreasing the junction field. Since a static electric field can only be produced by a suitable placement of electrical charge, how and where are the extra charges introduced, which must necessarily take part in any modification of the junction field by the applied voltage? What happens, in fact, is this: When a reverse bias is applied, the mobile charges in the quasi-neutral region adjacent to either side of the depletion layer move back from the junction, widening the depletion region and "uncovering," or no longer compensating, the charge of the fixed, ionized impurities in the additional width of depletion region. These additional fixed charges are responsible for the increase of junction field and potential difference. A similar but inverse action, of course, accompanies a forward bias.

This situation, where two regions of opposite mobile charge carriers are separated by a layer devoid of mobile charge, is very similar to that existing in a charged capacitor or condenser, where the plates have a high density of mobile charge and are separated by a space free of mobile charge (although, to be sure, in a condenser this space is usually free of *fixed* charge, as well). Therefore, we might expect a biased junction to act somewhat like a capacitor; furthermore, since the depletion-layer width changes with applied voltage, we might expect the junction capacitance to change with applied voltage, just as the capacity of a condenser changes as the plate separation is varied. Indeed, such effects do occur, and are measured by observing the *alternating* current which flows when small alternating voltages, in addition to the reverse bias, are impressed on the junction. Measurements of this effect yield valuable information about the junction width and the way in which the ionized impurity atoms are distributed throughout the depletion layer. It should be added that the uniform distribution of donors on the N side and acceptors on the P side, each sharply terminating at the junction, is an appropriate description of *abrupt* junctions. On the other hand, other distributions are possible, such as the gradual transition in the *graded* junction, and lead to somewhat different characteristics. This is true especially in the junction capacitance, which now varies as the inverse cube root of the applied voltage, rather than as the inverse square root as in the case of abrupt junctions.

Although our primary concern here is fundamental electron behavior rather than circuitry, let's digress for a moment to consider briefly the use of a junction diode rectifier in one basic circuit application, the transformation of alternating to direct current. The simplest circuit for this task, shown in Fig. 7.4, consists of an alternating current source S with peak voltage V_0, a rectifier L, and a resistive load R, all connected in series. The symbol shown for a rectifier—a closed or open arrowhead in contact with a flat plate—

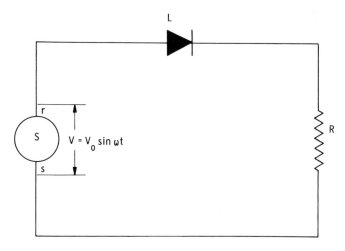

Figure 7.4

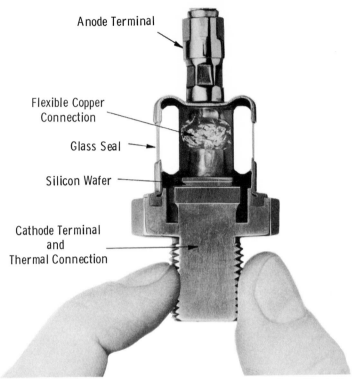

Anode Terminal

Flexible Copper
Connection

Glass Seal

Silicon Wafer

Cathode Terminal
and
Thermal Connection

(Westinghouse Electric Corporation)

Cutaway photograph of a commercial silicon diode. The semiconductor body and contacts, the flexible copper connection to prevent strains by differential expansion, and the hermetically sealed glass wall are indicated. The stud at bottom serves as both an electrical and a thermal contact; the connection to which it is joined is usually water-cooled. This unit will carry about 200 amperes, and withstand a reverse voltage as high as 1000 volts. The junction, located within the silicon wafer, is not discernible in this photograph.

is to be interpreted as indicating that current flows readily, that is, in the forward direction, when the arrowhead terminal is positive with respect to the plate terminal. We must bear in mind here the convention, often confusing to the newcomer, that the direction of current flow in a circuit is always assumed to be that of a flow of positive particles; since current flow in metals (or vacuum tubes, for that matter) is always carried by negatively charged electrons, the electron flow is opposite in direction to the conventional current flow. Therefore, the arrowhead of our symbol is to be identified with the P region of our junction device, and the plate with the N region.

In Fig. 7.4, when the source voltage, given here by V_0 sin wt, is such as to make r positive and s negative, the arrowhead will be positive with respect to the plate. Thus the junction is forward-biased and can be considered approximately as a closed switch; the voltage across the load R will be practically equal to the source voltage, and the current will be about the same as if the load were connected directly to the source. When the source voltage changes sign, the rectifier becomes reverse-biased, and very little current flows, most of the voltage appearing across the rectifier and very little across the load. Therefore, the current flow in the load and voltage across the load are predominantly unidirectional, or *direct*, as opposed to the *alternating* voltage of the source. Filters could be added, if necessary, to reduce the variations in load current during the cycle of applied voltage variation. In actual practice, the load R might be an electroplating bath where, since reverse current corresponds to removal of material from the specimen rather than plating onto it, it is essential that the current flow be predominantly unidirectional, although complete constancy is not necessary.

8

Solid State
Citizens

WE HAVE SEEN that in a forward-biased junction the current is carried almost entirely by majority carriers. On crossing the junction, these become minority carriers, representing an increase in minority carrier concentration above the normal equilibrium value characteristic of the particular material and temperature. They also represent an increase in the local concentration of excess charge, positive in the N region and negative in the P region. To maintain the region's charge neutrality, there must also be an equal increase of concentration of the oppositely charged majority carriers. Considered another way, an increase in minority carrier concentration results in a temporary net excess of charge. This, in turn, sets up an electric field of proper direction to attract majority carriers from surrounding regions, reducing the net excess charge and the field. In the regions thus depleted of majority carriers, a net excess charge is left, which attracts majority carriers from still more distant regions. This "chain reaction" continues until we reach the metallic contact connecting the region to the external circuit. This contact is the ultimate source of the majority carriers required to compensate the charge of the added minority carriers.

The process continues until the field is reduced not quite to zero, but to a value which will attract majority carriers at a rate just equal to the influx of minority carriers. Thus the resulting increases in concentration are almost equal for both types of carriers, the net excess being sufficiently small that charge neutrality, or exactly zero net excess, is a reasonable approximation. Increasing both types of carrier concentrations in a semiconductor above their normal equilibrium values is a process called *injection*. Since injection is essential in the operation of such devices as transistors, let's examine this process in some detail.

For the time being, let's assume that these excess injected carriers do not recombine within the body of the material. In this case, although the holes that flow from the *P* region across the junction into the *N* region are electrically compensated by extra majority electrons entering by way of the metallic contact, nonetheless they constitute a local increase in the hole concentration or density. These holes then begin to diffuse farther away from the junction into the *N* region. The extra electrons, required to neutralize the excess charge of holes, diffuse along with them. This tends to reduce the localization of the excess carrier concentration, while at the same time maintaining approximate charge neutrality everywhere. As diffusion continues, with additional minority holes introduced at the junction and compensating majority electrons at the metallic contact, the concentration of both electrons and holes gradually rises everywhere in the *N* region.

Since we assumed no recombination in the bulk of the material, we might be tempted to believe that in this case the excess carrier concentration would increase indefinitely—a conclusion to be viewed with at least mild distrust. Our assumption was actually weasel-worded, allowing for the possibility of recombination occurring at the surfaces of the material, particularly that surface to which the metallic contact is made to the external circuit. As we mentioned earlier, at places where the crystal structure is distorted, the lifetime is usually poor or, equivalently, the recombination rate is high; the transition from the semiconductor crystal lattice to that of the metallic contact—which in fact is hardly ever a single crystal of the metal, although even then it would differ from the semiconductor—is certainly a gross distortion of the lattice. Accordingly, the recombination rate there is very high, and the holes that reach this contact immediately recombine with electrons drawn in from the external circuit.

This recombination at the metallic contact limits the rise in carrier concentration which otherwise would occur, and eventually a steady state is reached, wherein all the holes injected into the N material at the junction flow to the metallic contact and recombine. Although this flow is aided by a small electric field, it is almost entirely a diffusion process. Since in this one-dimensional steady-state flow, the net rate of hole transport across any plane parallel to the junction must be the same, it follows from the earlier discussion of diffusion that the concentration gradient of the holes must be the same everywhere. These conditions are satisfied if the hole concentration in the N region decreases uniformly from its value at the junction to zero at the metallic contact. We must emphasize that this conclusion (that the hole flow across all planes parallel to the junction is equal, no matter what their distance from the junction) is dependent on our initial assumption of no recombination in the bulk of the material.

In order to preserve charge neutrality, the excess concentrations of electrons and holes must be equal everywhere; the concentration of both electrons and holes must decrease linearly from the junction toward the metallic contact. We might conclude that there would then also be a diffusive flow of electrons away from the junction, presumably equal to the hole flow, if the diffusive properties of both carriers were identical. However, this does not actually occur, because an electric field is built up in the bulk material, which is sufficient not only to overcome the tendency for diffusive flow of electrons away from the junction, but also to provide a flow of electrons in the N region *toward* the junction. These electrons are urged across the junction by the high field within, and become minority electrons injected into the P region, exactly analogous to the holes injected into the N region. Since the electron concentration in the N region is much higher than the hole concentration—usually three or more orders of magnitude higher—even a very small electric field acting on this large number of carriers is enough to cause the necessary electron flow. This small field aids the diffusive flow of holes very slightly, but the effect is not significant.

How is this electric field produced? Let's imagine, for a moment, that the concentrations of excess holes and electrons (excess, that is, above the equilibrium values) were exactly equal, so that strict charge neutrality prevailed, and that these excess concentrations decreased linearly from junction to metallic contact, as described before. There would then be exactly zero electric field everywhere in the N region, and because of the concentration gradient, both holes and electrons in the N region would immediately begin to diffuse from the junction to the metallic contact. However, while the holes are replaced by those injected at an equal rate across the junction from the P region, the diffusing electrons are not replaced. In fact, the electron supply in this region is further depleted by migration into the junction and across it to the P region, where the electrons become minority carriers, as mentioned before. This reduction of electron concentration results in an accumulation of net positive charge next to the junction, which establishes a small electric field in the N region. The field is just sufficient to overcome the diffusive flow of electrons toward the metallic contact and to maintain the electron supply against losses to the junction and the P region. The necessary deviation from absolute neutrality is small enough so that our assumption that the hole transport is entirely diffusive is still a good approximation. Therefore, our idea of a concentration of holes decreasing linearly from junction to metallic contact is still nearly correct. Our assumption that all external applied voltage appears across the junction depletion region, however, is affected by the presence of this electric field in the quasi-neutral N region, because a little of this voltage now appears as a potential drop or voltage difference between the N side of the junction and the metallic contact. But we can ignore this effect if the N region is thin enough; the thicker this region, the greater the voltage lost in maintaining the electric field in it. For this reason, it is usually desirable to keep both the N side and the P side of the device as thin as possible.

So far, we have a linear decrease of hole concentration from a finite value at the junction boundary to zero at the metallic contact, resulting in a diffusive transport of holes. The rate of hole flow, as well as of electron flow, is the same across all planes parallel to the junction, and the sum of these two flow rates, which need not be equal, is the total current flow through the device, of course. The hole current (that is, the number of holes entering the N region from the junction) is proportional to the hole concentration in the P region. This, in turn, is determined by the concentration of acceptor impurities there, while the electron current is similarly determined by the donor density in the N region.

What happens if we drop the assumption that no recombination occurs within the body of the material? In this case, not all holes injected into the N region at the junction will reach the metallic contact; some will recombine along the way, and in doing so remove both an electron and a hole. The same thing will happen to the electrons entering the N region from the metallic contact. This action will affect our previous picture of the current in several ways.

First, it is obvious that the hole density everywhere away from the junction will now be somewhat less than before; charge neutrality will then insure that the electron density is likewise lowered everywhere to match.

Second, the hole flow is no longer the same across all planes parallel to the junction; because the rate of hole efflux from the region between two such planes, that is, across the plane farther away from the junction, will be less than the influx rate across the other plane. The rate at which holes have recombined within this region represents the difference. This means that the fraction of total current in the N region carried by holes is no longer constant throughout that region, being a maximum adjacent to the junction, and decreasing toward the metallic contact. Conversely, the fraction of current carried by the electrons increases correspondingly from junction to metallic contact. Of course, the thinner we make the N region and the higher we can make the carrier lifetime, that is, the lower the recombination rate, then the larger will be the fraction of current carried by holes everywhere in the N region away from the junction. This point is of relatively minor importance in the operation of a diode, but it is fundamental in the action of a transistor, as we will see shortly.

The third difference caused by recombination is that since the hole current decreases the farther we go away from the junction, so must the hole concentration gradient. The concentration of holes no longer varies linearly with a constant gradient from junction to contact, but rather is exponential, both concentration and gradient decreasing from junction to contact. The value of the hole concentration at the edge of the junction will be the same whether or not recombination occurs; this follows from our earlier assumption that the hole densities at opposite edges of the junction are in equilibrium with each other. Everywhere else in the N region, however, the hole density is reduced by the presence of recombination.

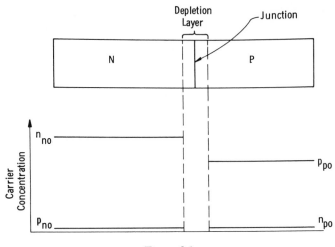

Figure 8.1

Our picture of the junction is now sufficient to allow us to calculate quantitatively the way the current varies with the voltage impressed across the junction. Figure 8.1 shows the distribution of majority and minority carriers in both regions when no voltage is impressed. In this case, we recall that the density of both carrier types is the equilibrium density, and therefore uniform in both regions outside the depletion layer surrounding the junction. The letters P and N refer, as before, to the conductivity type, or nature of impurity content, of each region; p and n refer to the density or concentration of holes or electrons, respectively, in either region, the subscripts p and n denoting the region under consideration. The further subscript o refers only to equilibrium conditions, and otherwise is omitted. For example, p_{no} is the density of holes in the N region at equilibrium. Finally, the subscript j will be used to denote values at the outer edges of the junction depletion layers.

As mentioned earlier, the electric field in the junction creates a difference of potential energy, or energy of position, between the N and P regions. This means that there is a difference in the total energy of electrons or holes (or any other charged particles, for that matter), depending on whether they happen to be on the N side or the P side. This energy difference is in addition to their *kinetic* energy as a result of their motion. For example, an automobile in motion has a kinetic energy equal to half the product of its mass and the square of its velocity; it also has a potential energy, measured with reference to some arbitrary elevation such as sea level, equal to the product of its mass m, the acceleration of gravity g, and its elevation h above the reference level. In the case of the junction, the potential difference results in one side being electrically "higher" than the other; but since holes and electrons are oppositely charged, the side higher for electrons, which happens to be the P side, is lower for holes, and vice versa.

If we consider a car coasting along a level road, and ignore friction, then both its velocity v and elevation h remain fixed, so that its total energy, $E = \frac{1}{2} mv^2 + mgh$, is also fixed. (Note that the content of this short equation required over fifty words for its verbal counterpart in the preceding paragraph.) If the car encounters a slight rise leading to a higher level stretch, it will coast up (provided v is large enough), losing some speed in the process and reaching the higher stretch at a lower velocity, which it then maintains. In this process, it exchanges kinetic energy for potential energy, the total energy remaining unchanged. Just so does an electron on crossing from the N to the P side lose kinetic energy, exchanging it for potential energy; a hole would in this case gain kinetic energy at the expense of potential energy. Here, just as we neglected friction in the car, we neglect energy losses from collisions.

The height of the potential hill at the junction, that is, the energy difference gained or lost by a unit of charge when it crosses the junction, we will denote by φ. The energy change of an electron or hole is then the product $q\varphi$, where q represents the charge of the electron or hole and is numerically 1.602×10^{-19} coulombs; φ is usually expressed in volts. Thus we can think of the charge q as a measure of the extent to which the electric field affects the potential energy of the electron or hole, just as the mass of the automobile is a measure of the extent to which the earth's gravitational field affects the potential energy of the automobile.

With this background, we can show the significance of our previous assumption that the densities of electrons on opposite sides of the junction are in thermal equilibrium; or, restated, that the number of electrons having total energy in excess of any given value is the same on both sides of the junction. (A further condition must also be added here: negative values of kinetic energy are not allowed; just as with the case of the automobile, negative kinetic energy demands an imaginary velocity.) Now, we said earlier that the fraction of electrons in the N region whose energy exceeds a given value E is almost exactly

$$e^{-E/kT}.$$

Therefore, in particular, the density of electrons in the N region whose energy exceeds $q\varphi$ is just

$$n_{no}e^{-q\varphi/kT}.$$

Since all electrons in the P region have a total energy of at least $q\varphi$ (because their potential energy is $q\varphi$ and their kinetic energy cannot be negative), our assumption says that the density n_{po} of electrons in the P region is equal to that of electrons in the N region of energy exceeding $q\varphi$, or

$$n_{po} = n_{no} \, e^{-q\varphi/kT}. \tag{8.1}$$

Since we will frequently use the quantity $e^{-q\varphi/kT}$, it will be more convenient to abbreviate this to the symbol λ; thus,

$$n_{po} = n_{no}\lambda. \tag{8.2}$$

A simple analogy may further clarify the relation between n_{no} and n_{po}. Imagine that two pails of water, whose bottoms are at different levels, are connected by a hose as in Fig. 8.2. We know that the water level in each pail will be the same when equilibrium is reached. Therefore, we can say that the amount of water having potential energy (or, in this case, elevation) above any given value is the same for both pails, as long as our given elevation is not below the bottom of either pail. This latter condition corresponds to our prohibition of negative kinetic energy. In similar fashion, the numbers of electrons having energies exceeding a given value are equal on both sides of the junction. However, this analogy, like nearly all others, is limited; for instance, neither pail contains any water molecules of energies corresponding to elevations above the water surface, while according to our earlier statement there is always a finite fraction

$$e^{-E/kT}$$

of electrons whose energy exceeds any chosen value E, no matter how high.

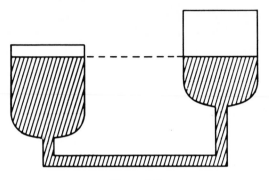

Figure 8.2

We have already seen that $n_{po} = \lambda n_{no}$; the same reasoning applied to the holes shows that

$$p_{no} = \lambda p_{po}. \tag{8.3}$$

Since if both sides of an equation are multiplied or divided by the same number, the products or quotients are also equal, let's divide both sides of the former of these equations by n_{no}; we then have

$$\lambda = \frac{n_{po}}{n_{no}}.$$

Similarly, division of the latter equation by p_{po} yields

$$\lambda = \frac{p_{no}}{p_{po}}.$$

Thus $\dfrac{n_{po}}{n_{no}}$ and $\dfrac{p_{no}}{p_{po}}$, each being equal to λ, must be equal to each other, or

$$\frac{n_{po}}{n_{no}} = \frac{p_{no}}{p_{po}}. \tag{8.4}$$

When we multiply each side of this equation by the product $n_{no}p_{po}$ we see that

$$n_{po}p_{po} = n_{no}p_{no}. \tag{8.5}$$

This relation states that the product of the equilibrium concentrations of electrons and holes is the same for both the P and the N material. Since the result did not depend on the level of impurity concentration in either region, we conclude that it should be true regardless of the type or presence of *doping* (a technical term for deliberately added impurities). That is, the product of the equilibrium hole and electron concentrations should be a constant which, although different for different semiconductors, will be the same for any one semiconductor regardless of the type or amount of doping. In particular, this product will be the same for doped material as for intrinsic (that is, pure) material.

Now, in intrinsic material, the concentrations of electrons and holes have been seen to be equal; if we denote this intrinsic concentration n_i, we can further write Eq. 8.5 as

$$n_{po}p_{po} = n_{no}p_{no} = n_i{}^2. \tag{8.6}$$

We cannot deduce from this the actual value of n_i. It depends on the nature of the material and on temperature. For germanium, it is about 3×10^{13} per cubic centimeter at room temperature; for silicon, about 6.5×10^{10}.

This relation suggests that an increase of n_{no} above its value n_i for intrinsic material, brought about by addition of donors, results in a corresponding decrease of p_{no}. The reason this occurs is that the increase in electron density provides more chance for any particular hole to recombine, thus increasing the recombination probability per unit time for each hole by the factor n_{no}/n_i. The total recombination rate is then proportional to the number of holes times the recombination rate for each hole, or to $n_o p_o$, where the type subscript has been omitted since the statement is valid in all cases. The generation rate is not significantly affected by the carrier or impurity concentrations, since these are usually negligible in comparison to the concentrations of the semiconductor atoms. Because in equilibrium the generation and recombination rates must be equal, we conclude that we should have $n_o p_o = n_i{}^2$, in agreement with our earlier result.

From Eq. 8.3, we can easily deduce the value of the contact potential φ. To simplify this, we will assume that the doping on both sides is so large that we can write approximately

$$p_{po} = P, \quad n_{no} = N,$$

where P and N now denote the numerical values of acceptor and donor concentration in their respective regions. (The exact relations, as evident from the condition of charge neutrality, would be

$$p_{po} - n_{po} = P, \quad n_{no} - p_{no} = N.$$

Using these instead of the preceding approximations complicates the arithmetic considerably, without adding much to our understanding.)

Now consider Eq. 8.3, or its equivalent form $\lambda = \dfrac{p_{no}}{p_{po}}$. Replacing p_{po} by its equivalent P, and P_{no} by n_i^2/n_{no}, and subsequently n_{no} by N, we have

$$\lambda = \frac{p_{no}}{p_{po}} = \frac{p_{no}}{P} = \frac{n_i^2/n_{no}}{P} = \frac{n_i^2}{NP}. \tag{8.7}$$

Since

$$\lambda = e^{-q\varphi/kT},$$

the logarithm of λ is just the exponent $-\dfrac{q\varphi}{kT}$ (remember this is the *natural* logarithm, here abbreviated *ln*, which is about 2.3 times the common logarithm to the base 10). Thus on taking the logarithm of each side of Eq. 8.7, we have

$$-\frac{q\varphi}{kT} = ln\frac{n_i^2}{NP} \tag{8.8}$$

or, multiplying both sides by $-\dfrac{kT}{q}$,

$$\varphi = -\frac{kT}{q} ln\frac{n_i^2}{NP} = \frac{kT}{q} ln\frac{NP}{n_i^2}, \tag{8.9}$$

since inverting a number, or dividing it into unity, only changes the sign of its logarithm. For germanium with $n_i = 10^{13}$, $N = P = 3 \times 10^{16}$, we find φ to be about one-third of a volt.

The situation resulting when a voltage is applied to the junction is shown in Fig. 8.3. Here the injection of carriers across the junction raises the minority carrier densities adjacent to the junction to n_{pj} and p_{nj}. We will assume that the applied voltage V is small enough that n_{pj}, although perhaps large compared to n_{po}, is still much smaller than p_{po} or n_{no}, and similarly for p_{nj}; and that the rate of flow of carriers across the junction is small enough that no appreciable reduction is thereby caused in the majority carrier densities on either side, which are then still p_{po} and n_{no}. As the injected minority carriers diffuse away, recombination reduces their densities exponentially with dis-

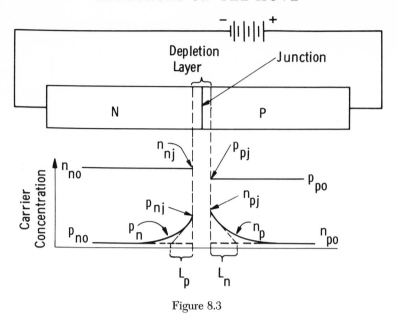

Figure 8.3

tance to n_{po} and p_{no} in regions far from the junction. The lines tangent at the junction to the graphs of p_n and n_p intersect the equilibrium-density levels at distances L_p and L_n from the junction edges; called the *diffusion length* for holes in the N region or electrons in the P region, respectively, these are the average distances over which a minority carrier diffuses before recombining. With our restrictions on V, the diffusion length is a constant depending on the material, but it is independent of the injected carrier density, since the majority carrier concentration, which, as we have seen, determines the recombination probability for each minority carrier, is unaltered. Incidentally, our figure shows the additional assumption, implicit in our discussion, that the thicknesses of the P and N regions are large compared to the diffusion lengths, which for germanium are typically one-tenth millimeter or so.

From Fig. 8.3 it is evident that the gradient of the electron concentration in the P region at the junction is the slope of this tangent line, or

$$\text{grad } n_p = \frac{n_{pj} - n_{po}}{L_n}. \tag{8.10}$$

As we have seen, the hole flux, or rate of flow, resulting from this is the product of the concentration gradient and the diffusion coefficient, D_e, for electrons, or

$$F_e = D_e \frac{n_{pj} - n_{po}}{L_n}. \tag{8.11}$$

Our fundamental assumption concerning the junction with an applied voltage was that the electron densities n_{pj} and n_{nj} were in equilibrium. Since the application of a voltage V has now changed the potential energy difference between opposite regions, we must replace φ in Eq. 8.1 by $\varphi - V$ (the negative sign resulting from our definition of forward voltage as the direction opposing the junction field). As a consequence, our assumption becomes

$$n_{pj} = n_{no} \, e^{-q(\varphi - V)/kT}. \tag{8.12}$$

From the elementary properties of exponents,

$$e^{-q(\varphi - V)/kT} = e^{(-q\varphi + qV)/kT} = e^{-q\varphi/kT} \cdot e^{qV/kT},$$

just as $x^5 = x^2 \cdot x^3$. If we now let β be an abbreviation for $e^{qV/kT}$, we can further write

$$n_{pj} = n_{no} \, e^{-q(\varphi - V)/kT} = n_{no} \, e^{-q\varphi/kT} \cdot e^{q\varphi/kT} = \lambda\beta \, n_{no}. \tag{8.13}$$

We now replace n_{pj} in the preceding diffusion flux equation by its value above, and n_{po} by its equivalent $\lambda \, n_{no}$; thus the electron diffusion flux is

$$F_e = \frac{D_e}{L_n} \left\{ \lambda\beta n_{no} - \lambda n_{no} \right\} = \frac{D_e}{L_n} \lambda n_{no} \, (\beta - 1). \tag{8.14}$$

This diffusive flow, as we mentioned earlier, is the total electron current in the P region, since the electric field outside the junction is very small. Because we have assumed no recombination within the junction region itself, this expression must be the electron flux at either edge of the junction. A similar expression,

$$F_h = \frac{D_h}{L_p} \lambda p_{po} \, (\beta - 1), \tag{8.15}$$

describes the oppositely directed hole flux. The sum of these fluxes, multiplied by q, the charge on each carrier, yields the desired expression for the total current:

$$I = q(F_e + F_h) = q\lambda \left(\frac{D_h P}{L_p} + \frac{D_e N}{L_n} \right)(\beta - 1), \qquad (8.16)$$

where we have replaced n_{no} and p_{po} by their approximate values N and P. On further substituting

$$\lambda = \frac{n_i^2}{NP},$$

we obtain finally

$$I = q\, n_i^2 \left(\frac{D_h}{NL_p} + \frac{D_e}{PL_n} \right)(e^{qV/kT} - 1), \qquad (8.17)$$

as the relation between impressed junction voltage and total current. Note that the N and P from

$$\lambda = \frac{n_i^2}{NP},$$

have been incorporated in the first parenthesis.

This equation shows at a glance not only which quantities determine the current, but in what way and by how much as well. For example, the diffusion lengths L_n and L_p affect the current; if each is doubled, then each term in the first parenthesis, and thus the current, will be halved. If only one is doubled, the resulting decrease in current will not be quite so great and will depend on the relative magnitudes of the two terms in this parenthesis. The effects of applied voltage and temperature are contained in the second parenthesis; for example, if V is positive, increasing V increases the exponent and the current. In particular, if V is more than about one-tenth volt and T is room temperature, then

$$e^{\ qV/kT} \gg 1.$$

In this case the 1 in Eq. 8.17 may be neglected, and it then follows that each further increase of V by one-fortieth volt multiplies the current by e, or 2.718^+.

Although formally derived for forward current flow, this equation holds for reverse-bias conditions, as well. When V is negative by more than a few tenths of a volt, the exponential term will be quite negligible, and the reverse current will be the constant value before the final parenthesis. This, obviously, is the reverse saturation current we have discussed before; we now have its magnitude as

$$I_{\text{sat}} = q\, n_i{}^2 \left(\frac{D_h}{NL_p} + \frac{D_e}{PL_h} \right). \tag{8.18}$$

In germanium, D_e is about 94 cm²/sec, D_h about 44 cm²/sec. With $N = P = 3 \times 10^{16}$, $n_i = 3 \times 10^{13}$, $L_n = L_p = 0.1$ mm, and $q = 1.602 \times 10^{-19}$ coulomb, we readily find that I_{sat} is about 60 microamps/cm².

Inspection of Eq. 8.17 reveals a fact that at first appears puzzling: The presence of N and P in the denominators of the expression for I suggests that increasing the impurity concentrations, which we know increases the carrier densities n_{no} and p_{po}, nevertheless *decreases* the current in either direction. Why is this? The answer lies in Eq. 8.9, which shows that an increase of N or P increases the height of the potential hill at the junction, and this effect more than overcomes the increase in current which would otherwise result from the increased carrier densities. Eq. 8.16 shows that if λ had not depended on impurity concentration, the hole or electron fluxes would, in fact, have been directly proportional to P and N, rather than inversely. In spite of the many assumptions involved, Eq. 8.17 agrees quite well with experimental results in those cases where the assumptions are expected to be valid.

The total current through the device is thus carried partly by electrons and partly by holes, and the relative fraction carried by each type of carrier is different at different locations in the device. In the N region next to the junction, the hole current away from the junction will depend on the hole density at the junction edge, which in turn will be proportional to the hole density in the P region, and thus finally to the density of acceptor impurities in the P material. In a similar manner, the electron current toward the junction at the N side will be proportional to the donor density in the N material. It would appear possible, then, to make the fraction of current in the N region, which is carried by holes, relatively large, or closer to unity, by making the donor density in the N region much smaller than the acceptor density in the P region. If the former is negligible compared to the latter, the current in the N region adjacent to the junction will be almost entirely carried by holes, and if the hole lifetime is long enough and the N region thin enough, the current will be almost entirely carried by holes everywhere in the N region. In the heavily doped P region, on the other hand, there will be very little enhancement of minority electron density by injection from the N region because the latter has so small a majority electron density as a result of its low donor content. Thus, in the P region almost all the current will be carried by majority holes.

At times, a literal account of a relatively complete theory, such as we have just outlined in some detail, obscures the underlying fact that, as with all physical science, this theory has been constructed by the minds of men. Such investigation, fully as exciting and rewarding as any that ever challenged Sherlock Holmes, continues with ever-increasing vigor. We would like to convey some of this sense of excitement and discovery by describing an experiment first performed only a few years ago, but now considered classic. It is known as the *Haynes-Shockley experiment,* for the two scientists who originally performed it.

The chain of events that led to this experiment is rather typical in scientific research. Investigation of the electrical properties of semiconductors had resulted in the formulation of a theory, or actually a collection of theories, which might adequately describe these properties. Although adequate description is a necessary requirement for an acceptable theory, it is never sufficient; there is always the nagging possibility that some further experimental result will show the theory to be completely askew. Faced with this possibility, the scientist is likely to ask, "Can I devise and carry out an experiment whose results will show, with as little ambiguity as possible, that this theory is (or is not) sound?" Presumably, just such a question was in the minds of Haynes and Shockley as they set about trying to demonstrate the existence, injection, and transport of holes in germanium.

Their arrangement is shown in Fig. 8.4. First, they made metallic contacts to both ends of a long, narrow rod of N-type germanium, and then applied a low voltage from a battery connected across these contacts. This produced an electric field in the rod. If any holes could be found in the material or added to it, this field would cause them to drift toward the negative contact. It would also cause a small constant flow of electrons, whether or not holes were present. Near the posi-

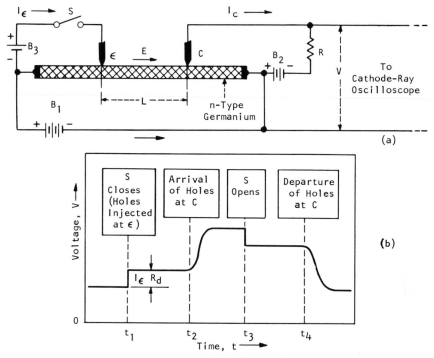

(Courtesy D. Van Nostrand Company, Inc., Princeton, New Jersey)

Figure 8.4

tive contact, they now placed the tip of a fine pointed metal wire in contact with the germanium surface. Theory indicated that a current of electrons in this wire, in a direction away from the germanium, would cause an emission or injection of holes into the germanium beneath the point, just as does the junction we have been discussing. The only other apparent possibility, if indeed holes were not produced, was merely an extraction of electrons. But if such a current were made to flow by connecting another battery between the wire and the positive end contact, how was it possible to tell if holes actually would be injected? Haynes and Shockley reasoned that one way would be to take advantage of the fact that if holes *were* introduced, it would take a measurable time for them to drift down the bar, as a result of the electric field, to some point farther "downstream" nearer the negative end contact. Therefore, they placed another fine wire probe against the germanium surface near the negative end contact, connecting this area to a current-measuring device, called a *cathode-ray oscillograph,* and a battery whose polarity was arranged to withdraw or collect from the germanium any holes that might possibly drift nearby. Their plan was to suddenly turn on the current at what they hopefully considered the "emitter" probe, and then observe any variations that took place at the "collector" probe.

From the outset, there were two rather obvious possibilities. If the bar were metal, such as copper, there would indeed be an observable effect at the collector when the current was turned on, for of the

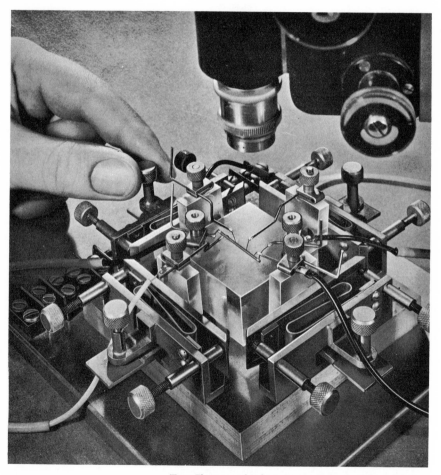

(From *Electrons and Holes in Semiconductors,* by William Shockley. Copyright 1950, D. Van Nostrand Company, Inc., Princeton, New Jersey)

The apparatus used in the Haynes-Shockley experiment. The germanium bar and its contacts are visible at the center of the photograph, as described in the text.

electrons that would flow out through the emitter, some would be replaced by electrons flowing in through the collector. However, this effect, the consequence of ordinary electron flow as described by Maxwell's equations, would be propagated from emitter to collector with a speed nearly that of light; there would be no observable time-lag between emitter current and corresponding collector current. The same effect was also to be expected in germanium; but if holes actually existed and were injected by the emitter, an additional change in collector current would occur later, once the cloud of injected holes had drifted to the collector. The observation of such a time-lag would be rather conclusive evidence that "something" was slowly drifting through the bar, giving very strong support to the hole theory. The beauty of this experiment, aside from its simplicity, lies in the fact that it is quite difficult to explain a positive result on any basis other than the existence of holes.

Haynes and Shockley actually observed a time-lag, providing brilliant confirmation of the existence of holes. Extensions of their experiment made it possible to measure the mobility and lifetime of holes, as well. The mobility is the quotient of the average velocity of drift, divided by the electric field; the latter is already known, and the former is given directly by the emitter-to-collector distance, divided by the observed travel time. By repeating the experiment several times, with the collector probe placed successively at a series of points along the bar, it is found that the larger the emitter-to-collector spacing, the fewer holes reach the collector as a result of recombination en route. From this information and the drift velocity just calculated, the average lifetime follows immediately.

THE JUNCTION TRANSISTOR

The ideas we have been discussing in this chapter and the previous one are practically applied in the operation of a *junction transistor*. Such a device, like other types of transistors, is capable of performing many of the functions of a vacuum tube.

The junction transistor consists of three semiconductor layers of alternating conductivity type, separated by two junctions, as shown in Fig. 8.5. The layer arrangement can be either *N-P-N* or *P-N-P*; both types are made. We will concentrate on the *P-N-P* structure, but let's

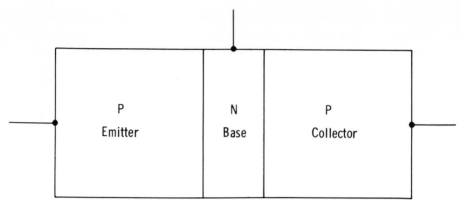

Figure 8.5

bear in mind that exactly analogous conditions hold for the *N-P-N*, simply by interchanging *N* with *P* and holes with electrons. The configuration looks like a ham sandwich, the outer *P* regions being the bread, the central *N* region the ham, and the junctions occurring where the bread is buttered. Regardless of the particular variety, *N-P-N* or *P-N-P*, the central region is called the *base;* one of the outer regions is the *emitter,* the other the *collector.* Leads, attached to metallic contacts to these two regions, complete the device. Usually the emitter is more heavily doped than either the base or the collector, so that the structure is not symmetrical.

The transistor's usefulness is due to the fact that a small amount of power in a circuit involving the emitter and base can control a much larger flow of power in a circuit between collector and base. This process of amplification also occurs, as we have already seen, in vacuum tubes by a somewhat different mechanism. In fact, as we mentioned, the transistor can perform nearly all the functions of a vacuum tube, although not necessarily as well; the two devices should be viewed as alternate possibilities, the merits of each depending on the particular application.

In operation, the emitter-base junction is biased in the forward direction by an external voltage source; the collector is reverse-biased relative to the base. In order to see how a voltage or current applied to the emitter circuit will affect the voltage and current at the collector, let's first examine the collector current when the emitter current is zero, for example, when the emitter is not externally connected to anything; it is then said to be "floating." The only active part of the transistor is then the *P-N* junction diode formed by the collector and base respectively. In a reverse-biased collector, the current flow will be the small reverse saturation current of the collector junction. This current will vary only slightly with collector-to-base voltage V_{cb} in a manner similar to the reverse saturation current of the diode, as shown in Fig. 7.3 of Chapter Seven. Such current consists of the minority holes in the base, which diffuse to the junction and are swept across, and of a similar current of minority electrons in the collector, which cross to the base. The amount of this current carried by holes is proportional to the density of holes in the base region. As we mentioned earlier in discussing the diode, this current is relatively small and nearly independent of collector voltage over fairly wide range.

Now, when the emitter is forward-biased, a current flows across the emitter-base junction, which may be shortened to *emitter junction*. This current consists of majority holes in the emitter region that, on crossing the junction, become minority carriers in the base, and also of majority electrons in the base that cross the junction toward the emitter, becoming minority carriers. We will be little concerned with these electrons, and will therefore leave them to their ultimate fate of recombination with the holes of the emitter. However, the behavior of the holes that reach the base is quite important to us. In the terms used in the previous section, these holes are "injected" into the base, and then diffuse away from the emitter junction and either recombine or eventually reach the collector junction. Those that do reach the collector junction are swept across to the collector, along with the holes which constitute the collector saturation current. The extra hole flow represents an increase in collector current as a result of the flow of emitter current; this is the fundamental action of a junction transistor.

It is apparent that of the total emitter current, only that fraction carried by holes from the emitter is useful in increasing the collector current. The electrons from base to emitter serve no purpose in the process, and therefore it is desirable to make the emitter current consist as largely as possible of holes from the emitter. As we saw in the preceding section, this can be done by having a much higher concentration of acceptor impurities in the emitter than of donors in the base, which results in a relatively high emitter hole density. Not all of the holes injected into the base reach the collector, since some re-combine on the way. For this reason it is desirable to have in the base as low a recombination rate as possible, or equivalently as high a lifetime, and further to make the distance from emitter to collector (the base width) very small. If we then let γ represent the fraction of the emitter current carried by holes, and β indicate the fraction of holes that cross the base and reach the collector junction, we can write the collector current, I_c, as

$$-I_c = \gamma\beta I_e + I_{c0}, \qquad (8.19)$$

where I_{c0} is the collector reverse leakage current, and I_e is the emitter forward current. Note that this β bears no relation to the β of Eq. 8.13. Clearly, γI_e is the current carried by those holes that cross the emitter junction into the base; hence, γ is called the *emitter efficiency*, since it describes how efficiently the emitter current is utilized in injecting holes into the base. Then $\gamma\beta I_e$ is the fraction of I_e which represents holes reaching the collector.

To make our explanation complete, we should add that there are some processes, not described here, in which the arrival of holes at the junction results in extra holes, and electrons, being produced there, and this further augments the collector current. If we let α^* be the factor by which these latter processes increase the collector hole current, we can write the collector current as

$$-I_c = \gamma\beta\alpha^* I_e + I_{c0} = \alpha I_e + I_{c0}. \qquad (8.20)$$

For a transistor operated under the conditions we have assumed, α^* is unity.

The product $\gamma\beta\alpha^*$, which we have represented by α, is called the current gain of the transistor. Since obviously γ and β are both less than unity, for our conditions α is also less than unity. In practice, γ and β can both readily be made to exceed 0.995, hence α can exceed 0.99.

It is evident that αI_e represents the fraction of the total emitter current I_e which ultimately results in an increase in the hole component of collector current. What about the remainder, $(1 - \alpha)I_e$? This comprises the electrons removed from the base by the small electron component of the emitter current, plus the additional electrons removed from the base by recombination of holes, which perish en route from emitter to collector. Both of these electron losses are made up by the electron current flowing into the base via the base contact. This base current must also take into account two mechanisms that add electrons to the base region; these are the flow of electrons from collector to base, and the electrons resulting from thermal generation, in the base, of hole-electron pairs, of which the holes flow across the collector junction into the collector. The total of these last two processes, of course, is just the reverse collector saturation current that we have called I_{c0}. With due regard for sign, the base current is then given by

$$I_b = I_{c0} - (1 - \alpha) I_e. \tag{8.21}$$

This equation, together with that previously stated for I_c, completely describes the current flow within the transistor. It is conventional to choose the signs so that a positive value for the current at any terminal represents a flow of positive charge into, or negative charge out of, that terminal. Thus, I_e describes a flow of electrons out of the emitter; I_c, the current in the lead attached to the collector, is the result of a flow of holes, or positive charge, across the collector junction into the collector, requiring negative charge to flow in, via the external circuit, for charge neutrality. This accounts for the minus sign preceding I_c. Similar considerations obtain for the signs in the expression for base current. Since the transistor as a whole must not accumulate electric charge, the sum of these currents must be zero, as we see from

$$I_e + I_b + I_c = I_e + I_{c0} - (1 - \alpha)I_e - \alpha I_e - I_{c0} = 0. \tag{8.22}$$

The current I_{c0} is considered a negative quantity here, in order to agree with Eq. 8.17 for the current in a diode, which conventionally is negative for reverse bias.

We have observed that when no emitter current flows, the collector current is just the small reverse saturation current I_{c0}, which is almost independent of collector voltage V_{cb}, because as long as the collector is more than a few tenths of a volt more negative than the base, it will collect all the holes that reach the collector junction. The number of these holes depends only on the thermal generation rate and the diffusion coefficient in the base, neither of which is appreciably affected by the collector voltage. As we might suspect, this is true even when the base hole concentration is increased by the presence of emitter current flow. Increasing the magnitude of the collector voltage widens the depletion region of the collector junction, but has negligible effect on the conditions within the base region. Thus, the collector current is essentially independent of collector voltage (provided this voltage is low enough that the multiplication processes, described by α^*, do not occur). The emitter current is also independent of collector voltage.

How are these currents affected by emitter voltage? We might expect at first that the relation between I_e and V_{eb} would be given by Eq. 8.17, since emitter and base comprise a forward-biased junction. In a sense this is true, but the equation must be modified to account for the effect on the emitter current of the presence of the nearby collector junction. This effect is shown in Fig. 8.6, illustrating the comparison between the hole concentration in the N region of the forward biased diode of Fig. 8.3 and that of the base of the *P-N-P* transistor. In this diode, the N region was assumed to be quite wide, so that the holes injected at the junction all recombined before reaching the metallic contact at the right. We saw before that in this case, as shown by the diode curve, the hole concentration decreases exponentially from its value P_{nj} at the junction as we go toward the right. We also saw that the hole concentration gradient at the junction is

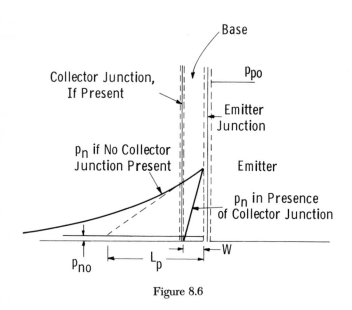

Figure 8.6

P_{nj}/L_p, where L_p is the diffusion length of holes. Obviously, if we want the collector junction to collect most of the injected holes, it is necessary to place it close enough to the emitter junction so that the holes can reach it before recombining; therefore, the emitter-collector distance, or base width W, should be small compared to L_p. In this case, we can—approximately—neglect recombination in calculating the hole distribution in the base. The situation in the base is then similar to that discussed in connection with the diode, when we assumed no recombination. The collector here absorbs all holes reaching it, just as the metallic contact did in the diode; again we find the hole concentration gradient varies linearly from its value P_{nj} at the junction to zero at the collector. Since the concentration P_{nj} is still assumed to be in equilibrium with the majority hole concentration in the emitter, its value is not changed by the presence of the collector. Therefore, it is evident that the hole concentration gradient at the junction is now P_{nj}/W, rather than P_{nj}/L_p as with the wide diode. The forward voltage-current characteristic of the emitter is then given approximately by replacing L_p of the diode Eq. 8.17 by W, yielding

$$I_e = q \, n_i{}^2 \left(\frac{D_n}{NW} \right) (e^{qV/kT} - 1), \tag{8.23}$$

where we have assumed P large enough that its reciprocal is negligible compared to that of N. Note that although the emitter is heavily doped to make holes carry most of the current, thus yielding high emitter efficiency, the actual magnitude of this current for a given voltage is primarily determined by base doping N rather than P. Somewhat similar modifications of the diode curve for reverse bias must be made to describe the reverse-biased emitter. Since this is not a normal condition of transistor operation, however, we mention it only in passing.

What about the behavior of a transistor when regarded from an external point of view? Since the transistor is a three-terminal device, we can specify three applied voltages, V_{eb}, V_{bc}, and V_{ce}, where each is measured between the terminals indicated by the subscripts. However, the sum of these three is always zero, so that specification of any two is sufficient. Similarly, three external currents, I_e, I_c, and I_b, flow in the three leads, but since the structure as a whole must not accumulate net charge, the sum of these currents is also zero; only two currents need be specified. Thus, to completely describe the state of operation, all we need choose is four quantities, two voltages and two currents. Of the nine possible sets, any two quantities may be arbitrarily given certain values; these are called *independent variables*. The remaining two are then determined by the equations we have developed, and are therefore called the *dependent variables*. Since there are six ways of choosing the independent pair, in all there are fifty-four ways of expressing the transistor characteristics in the general form of two dependent variables, either voltage or current, being expressed as functions of two independent variables, likewise voltages or currents. The mode selected varies with the expected application, and this accounts for the somewhat bewildering variety in which transistor characteristics are presented.

Our development of the theory leads naturally to our choosing as independent variables the collector voltage and the emitter current, and expressing the emitter voltage and collector current in terms of these. However, in doing this we must be careful to specify quite accurately both emitter and collector currents, because the base current is the difference of these currents. Furthermore, since our analysis shows emitter and collector currents to be nearly equal, they must be accurately known for their difference to be meaningful. Partly for this reason, this mode of specification is usually discarded in favor of one that gives the base current explicitly as one of the four variables.

We can readily predict the form of the dependence of collector current I_c on collector-to-base voltage V_{cb} for different constant values of emitter current I_e; for each I_e the value of I_c should be represented by a horizontal straight line independent of V_{cb}, and having an ordinate αI_e. The same plot, repeated for different equally spaced values of I_e, yields a family of parallel horizontal lines whose spacing depends on the value of α in that region; if α is constant, all these lines should be of equal spacing. (For comparison, Fig. 8.7 is a manufacturer's curve sheet for a typical *P-N-P* germanium alloy junction transistor, type 2N206. The I_c versus V_{cb} curves can be seen to be exactly as described above.)

At this point we have reached our goal of describing the electrical behavior of the junction diode and the transistor in terms of the

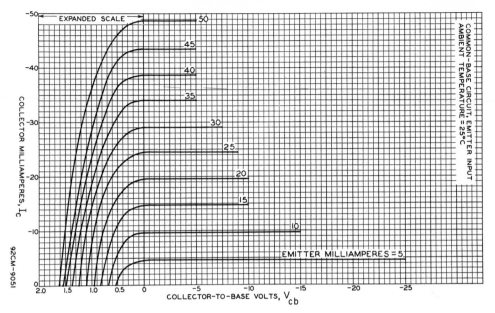

Figure 8.7

important internal processes which occur in their operation. In formulating this description, we should remember that for both devices we have used an idealized model that neglects many of the physical facts. For example, we have assumed that all current flows are one-dimensional; that is, that current always flows parallel to one specific direction. This is never true for the transistor, strictly speaking, for a glance at Fig. 8.5 makes it obvious that since the emitter and collector entirely bound both sides of the base region, any base current must necessarily flow in vertically from the top or bottom of the base. Many other simplifying assumptions have similarly been made, explicitly or implicitly, in our description.

In spite of this idealization, our eventual results turn out to agree rather well with experiment, as we have seen. The reason for this is that we have been selective in our assumptions, deciding the effects to include and those to ignore on the basis of which ones had been found by past experiments to be significant. Based on this experimental background, our description includes the important fundamental phenomena, but it should not be taken as a complete description of transistor operation.

When the scientist tries to understand and explain a new phenomenon, he usually chooses, just as we did, an idealized model that includes the most significant processes and ignores the less important ones. The choice of which must be included and which can safely be discarded is made on the basis of general experience, specific experimental data, and intuition. Here, perhaps as nowhere else, the scientist displays his physical insight and imagination.

New Modes
of Motion

9

Speeding
–Under Control

ALTHOUGH ALL MOTIONS of electric charge may properly be considered as electric currents, frequently it happens that the current is of itself much less significant than some of the other aspects of the motion. In this chapter we will explore the operation of three types of devices in which the currents associated with the charges in motion are of only minor importance: charged-particle accelerators, photoelectric image tubes, and lasers.

The story of the cyclotron might be said to begin in the late 1920's, when investigations of the nature of the atomic nucleus were beginning to yield exciting results. It became pretty clear that the nucleus was a very small—even on an atomic scale—aggregation of particles, protons and neutrons, the existence of the neutron discovered in 1932. As we have seen, there are repulsive electrostatic forces between particles of like charge, and on this basis we would expect such an assemblage to disintegrate immediately. However, in addition to the electrostatic forces there are other "short range" forces that become significant when the particles in question approach each other within 10^{-10} centimeters or so, and these forces bind the nucleus into an entity that is very stable indeed.

Now investigating the nature of such a structure is no simple matter. An obvious attack would be to bombard the nucleus with high-speed particles—protons, neutrons, or alpha particles, for example—in the expectation that the resulting collision would break the nucleus into rapidly moving fragments. The identities of these fragments might then be established by measuring such properties as mass, charge, and velocity. Since natural radioactive disintegration, in which certain atomic nuclei spontaneously emit particles and thus change into different nuclei, offers one source of such particles, many early experiments used sources of this kind. The method was not very satisfactory, however, because the emitted particles came out in all directions and with energies not subject to alteration or control.

It was obvious that a one-directional beam of particles of uniform and controllable energy would be far more desirable. The search for a means of producing such a beam naturally divided into two separate parts: a source of particles of the desired type at low energies, and then some means of accelerating these particles to much higher energies. It was soon recognized that the source depends on the particular particle; for example, for electrons, a heated metal filament in vacuum; for protons, an electric arc discharge in hydrogen, or in deuterium for deuterons. The means of acceleration utilizes the same forces discussed in Chapter Four, forces derived from electric or magnetic fields.

The simplest arrangement for such a particle accelerator has a source of particles at one end of a long narrow tube, typically six inches in diameter and twenty feet long, the exact dimensions depending on the energies to be produced and on other factors as well. A voltage, or potential difference, is produced by a suitable electric system—a very high voltage transformer or generator, for example— and applied between the particle source and an electrode at the opposite end of the tube, thus producing within the tube an electric field that will accelerate the particles along the tube. Obviously, the tube must be evacuated because otherwise the accelerated particles lose energy and change direction as they collide with gas molecules within the tube. It is also clear that the tube must be a very good electrical insulator so that the extremely large voltage along it can be sustained without enormous current flow in the tube walls. The particles from the source are thus accelerated toward the electrode at the other end of the tube; there they may pass through a hole in this

Outside view of a Van de Graaff generator. The high-voltage end of the tube is within the pear-shaped enclosure, which is pressurized with a suitable gas to provide adequate electrical insulation against the four and a half million volt potential attained inside. The target and the lower end of the tube, within the building, are at ground potential. The high-voltage end may be made to have either polarity.

electrode, emerging as a parallel concentrated beam of particles with a quite uniform energy which can be controlled by adjusting the total voltage applied to the tube. Many early accelerators were of this type. Those using high voltage transformers were called *Cockroft-Walton* systems, named for the inventors; *van de Graaff* accelerators, also named for the inventor, used static electricity generated by friction and transported by moving conveyor belts.

These systems, particularly the van de Graaff, had the desirable property of allowing very precise control of the output energy. They were employed in many investigations of nuclear reactions, especially in determining the minimum or *threshold* energy necessary to make a specific process occur. But they suffered from one very important limitation: the highest energy they could produce corresponded to the highest voltage that could be employed, and this was limited by the onset of *corona discharge,* or *arc discharge*—artificial lightning— either within or outside the tube. In practice this limit is about ten million volts. The desire for particle energies far higher than this appeared to require a new approach to the acceleration problem.

The cyclotron, developed in 1930 by Ernest O. Lawrence of the University of California, provided such an approach. This device utilizes both an electric and a magnetic field; the former exerts on a charged particle a force in the direction of the field, and the latter exerts on a *moving* charge a force at right angles to both the magnetic field and the direction of the motion. The essential elements of a cyclotron are a pair of hollow metal electrodes, called *Dees* because of their resemblance to the printed letter D. Their configuration can be described by imagining a short squat metal tube, the top and bottom enclosed by circular plates and the whole then cut along the tube axis into two equal pieces. The arrangement is shown in Fig. 9.1. A source of the desired charged particles is placed near the center, midway between the Dees. The entire apparatus is evacuated and placed in a strong magnetic field perpendicular to the plane faces. Finally, an alternating voltage is applied between the two Dees.

Consider the path of a particle—a proton, for example—emitted from a source at a time when the voltage between the Dees is at a maximum. The field produced between the Dees by this voltage will accelerate the proton toward the negative Dee; on entering the Dee, however, the proton finds itself in a region essentially free of electric field, because almost all of the electric field occurs in the gap between the Dees. The proton would thus continue in a straight line at the speed it had on entering the Dee, were it not for the presence of the magnetic field. Since this field is parallel to the axis while the proton's motion is perpendicular to this direction, the magnetic field exerts on the proton a force parallel to the plane of the Dees and perpendicular to the direction of the proton's path. The

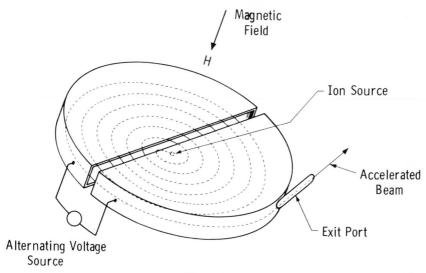

Figure 9.1

force bends the path of the proton into a circle centered on the axis, and the centrifugal force resulting from the curved path is just balanced by the centripetal force produced by the field. The proton thus describes a semicircular path within the Dee, emerging into the gap once again with a velocity equal to that with which it entered the Dee, but oppositely directed.

If the electric field in the gap were still the same as it was at the initial traverse, the force on the proton would now be opposite to its velocity, and the proton would be decelerated. However, the voltage between the Dees is alternating, and if the period of alternation is made just equal to the time required for one revolution of the proton in its circular path, the voltage at this time will be a maximum, as before, but of opposite polarity. Thus, the proton is again accelerated, adding to its velocity as it crosses the gap for the second time. This process is repeated many times, perhaps a few hundred, the proton gaining energy at each successive crossing of the gap, and describing ever larger half-circles in each Dee. As long as the proton energy is not too large, the time taken for each semicircular path is independent of its size; for the centripetal force produced by the magnetic field is given by

$$f_1 = \frac{Hev}{c}, \tag{9.1}$$

while the centrifugal force required to hold the proton in its orbit is

$$f_2 = mv\omega. \qquad (9.2)$$

Equating these forces and dividing both members of the resulting equation by mv yields:

$$\omega = \frac{He}{mc}, \qquad (9.3)$$

showing that ω, the angular velocity with which the path is described, does not depend on v, the proton velocity. The time required to complete a circular orbit $(2\pi/\omega)$ is thus also independent of velocity. In the above equation, H is the magnetic field intensity, m and e are the mass and charge of the proton, and c is the velocity of light.

This constancy of orbital time means that if the frequency of the alternating voltage applied to the Dees is held fixed, then each time the proton crosses the gap the electric field will be of the right polarity to accelerate it still further. Thus the proton spirals outward, continually gaining energy, and eventually emerges through an exit at the edge of one of the Dees. The resulting beam of high-energy protons may then be used for whatever purpose is at hand.

If the particles are accelerated to sufficiently high energies, the relativistic increase in mass with velocity becomes appreciable, causing Eq. 9.2 to be no longer accurate. In this energy range, the frequency of the Dee voltage must be decreased somewhat as the energy rises in order to add energy at each crossing. This is accomplished with a device called a *synchrocyclotron*. In its operation a group of particles is emitted into the Dees as in the conventional cyclotron, but since the frequency is made to vary as the group is accelerated, no further particles can be added until this group has run its entire course of several thousand revolutions and has been ejected from the system. The frequency is then increased to its initial value, suitable for the introduction of a new group of particles. Typically this process recurs several hundred times per second, yielding an output comprising periodic bursts of particles, rather than a continuous stream as in the conventional cyclotron.

There are two factors that make the cyclotron unusable for electrons, both direct results of the lower mass of the electron. The first is that the required frequency of the Dee voltage would be unreasonably high; this frequency is given directly from Eq. 9.3 by $\omega/2\pi$, and evidently depends inversely on particle mass. For protons, the frequency is usually of the order of ten megacycles, a quite reasonable figure. For electrons, it would then exceed 18,000 megacycles for the same magnetic field. The other factor is that the relativistic mass increase would be more serious for electrons than for heavy particles. However, an electron accelerator somewhat similar in principle to the cyclotron has been constructed, in which the acceleration is brought about not by an applied voltage but by a changing magnetic field. In this device, called a betatron (since electrons are also known as beta particles), a low-energy electron stream is introduced into the side of an evacuated doughnut-shaped chamber through whose central hole an alternating magnetic field of perhaps a few hundred cycles per second is produced by an electromagnet.

We recall that the law of electromagnetic induction states that a changing magnetic field anywhere in space necessarily produces an electric field as well. A form of this law, applicable to the case at hand, states that if any closed path in space encircles a changing magnetic flux, then around this path there is an electromotive force (that is, a unit charge transported once around this path gains an amount of energy) proportional to the time rate at which the total flux encircled by the path is changing. Here the path is a circular one within the doughnut, always in the center of the dough, so to speak; this of course encircles all the flux through the central hole. During the cyclic change of this flux from a maximum in one direction to a maximum in the opposite direction, an electromotive force acts to accelerate electrons continuously around this path. In a typical case electrons travel several hundred thousand times around this orbit, gaining a few hundred volts each trip, and producing an electron beam of some hundreds of millions of electron-volts energy.

It is also found convenient to use the betatron principle as part of a cascade process for accelerating protons to energies as high as several billion electron volts. Beams of high-energy particles produced by these or similar machines have been indispensable tools in the investigation of nuclear structure.

Among many phenomena that demonstrate the intimate connection between electrons and light, two are of fundamental importance for a class of devices we might call, collectively, photoelectric image tubes. The first of these phenomena is the photoelectric effect: when light quanta of sufficient energy strike a material surface in vacuum, electrons are liberated from the surface into the surrounding vacuum. The second effect is called fluorescence: when electrons strike the surface of suitably prepared materials, light is emitted from the material at the point of impact. Let's first investigate these effects briefly, and then see how they are utilized in an image tube.

In discussing the photoelectric effect it is necessary to consider the electronic structure of the material in question. The simplest case is that of a gas, which we can consider as a collection of widely separated and non-interacting molecules; the occasional collisions between molecules, whose result is the internal pressure of the gas, can be ignored for our present purposes. In each of these molecules the electrons, as we have already seen, have certain well-defined energies characteristic of the particular molecule. We can think of each electron as following a path, or orbit, within the molecule, the particular path being associated with the energy of the electron. Only a certain special set of orbits, and correspondingly of energies, are permitted. When all the electrons occupy the lowest allowed set of energies, the molecule is said to be in its ground state, and this is usually the case for materials at room temperature.

Some of the electrons may be raised to higher energy levels by several different processes. One such process utilizes the action of light. This should not be surprising, since light, as an electromagnetic wave, consists of rapidly varying electric and magnetic fields, which we have seen can exert forces on an electron and thus change its energy. An adequate quantitative explanation of this process, however, cannot be built on this simple classical idea, but requires quantum theory (and, in turn, the experimental results provided much of the initial verification of the quantum theory when it was first proposed by Max Planck in 1900). One result of this theory is that light must be thought of as a stream of small packets or quanta, each having an energy that depends on the wavelength λ or frequency v of the light. This energy E is given by

$$E = hv = \frac{hc}{\lambda}, \tag{9.4}$$

where, as before, c is the velocity of light, and h is a universal constant, called Planck's constant. The value of c is very nearly 3×10^{10}

cm/sec; and for a wavelength of 5000 Å or 5×10^{-5} cm, about that of green light, the energy is 2.479 electron-volts. When a light quantum interacts with an electron, its entire energy, never just part of it, is transferred to the electron. Depending on the wavelength of the light, this energy may only raise the electron to a level higher than its ground state but still corresponding to an orbit confined to the molecule; if the energy is sufficient, however, the electron may be entirely freed from the molecule, and this ionizes the electron.

When the molecules are more closely packed into a solid—by lowering the temperature, for instance—the increased interaction between molecules alters the details of the allowed orbits and energy levels. Nevertheless, in this case too the electrons within the solid are permitted only certain discrete energy values and orbits, each of which corresponds to one of the values and orbits in the original molecule. In fact, the solid may conveniently be thought of as a giant molecule. As in the case of a gas, light quanta may excite electrons from the ground state to higher energy levels (as in the process of photoconductivity, for example, discussed in connection with semiconductors) or, if the quanta are sufficiently energetic, the electron may be completely ejected from the solid. The minimum energy required for this is characteristic of the material (and sometimes of its surface treatment, as well) and is called the work function, as explained in Chapter Six. Its value is usually a few electron-volts. For quanta of energy less than the work function, no photoelectrons are ejected; for quantum energies exceeding the work function, the emergent electrons will have a kinetic energy up to but no greater than the quantum energy in excess of the work function. Even in the latter case, not every quantum will eject a photoelectron because some of the excited electrons will be directed away from the surface into the solid and recaptured within the material. Others may be captured before reaching the surface even though they are directed toward it. The average number of photoelectrons per quantum of sufficient energy, called the quantum efficiency of the material as a photoelectric emitter, is seldom much more than 10 percent. To obtain such efficiency in the visible spectrum requires rather complex mixtures of materials and elaborate processing.

Since the work functions of most materials are about one to perhaps four volts, it can be seen from Eq. 9.4 that only light of wavelength less than about ten or twelve thousand Å has quanta of sufficient energy to eject photoelectrons. On the other hand, wavelengths that are much shorter than, say, 2000 Å are readily absorbed by the atmosphere and hence are not usually present in natural radiation at the earth's surface. Furthermore, because quanta corresponding to these shorter wavelengths have energies considerably greater than most work functions, they will produce photoelectrons of rather high kinetic energy, or initial velocity. We will see later that such high initial velocities present some practical difficulties.

The human eye, an excellent light-sensitive system, is photochemical rather than photoelectric; that is, its action involves reversible chemical reactions whose progress is affected by absorption of the energy of the light quanta present. In this case, too, there is a minimum necessary quantum energy, and similarly there are practical limitations to the maximum usable energy; these combine to limit the spectral range of the eye to wavelengths between about 4000 to 7000 Å. The significant point here is that the wavelength region in which either the eye or artificial photoelectric devices can operate is not a matter of caprice but a consequence of both theoretical and practical limitations of nature; the regions for both devices are essentially the same within a factor of about two.

Fluorescence, as we said before, is the production of light by the impact of sufficiently energetic electrons on some suitable substance. Undoubtedly the most familiar example is a television picture, which is produced by a small moving spot of light generated by the impact of a focused beam of high-speed electrons on a phosphor, a layer of fluorescent material on the inner face of the picture tube. Fundamentally, the process of fluorescence is again the consequence of the electronic structure of the material. We said previously that in materials at or near room temperature, the electrons usually occupy the lowest possible set of energy states, but some of these can be raised to higher levels in several ways. We have already considered the action of incident light as one process. Impingement of a high-speed electron is another method. When such an electron strikes a material, it gives up its energy in a series of collisions within the material. Although most of these collisions result only in converting the electron's kinetic energy into heat, in suitable materials an appreciable fraction of the energy may be used to raise other electrons from the ground state to higher "excited" energy states.

These excited electrons remain in their higher energy states for an average time, called the decay time or persistence, which may range from a microsecond to several seconds, depending on the material. They then divest themselves of their excess energy by suddenly returning to their ground state, or a state of nearly equal energy; in this downward transition the extra energy is given up as a single quantum of radiation, and if the material is chosen to have suitable energy levels, the radiation will be in the visible spectrum. Because the incident high-energy electron may make a great many collisions within the material before dissipating its energy, a single incident electron may produce several quanta of radiation—perhaps an average of as many as fifty. The wavelength or color of this radiation depends on the energy levels involved, and phosphors can be found for almost any desired color. Just as photoelectric materials are carefully controlled mixtures of several substances, so are practical phosphors.

Now let's imagine a photoelectric image tube as an evacuated space in the shape of a circular, cylindrical glass tube, with flat glass end-plates, as shown in Fig. 9.2. On the inside of one end-plate there

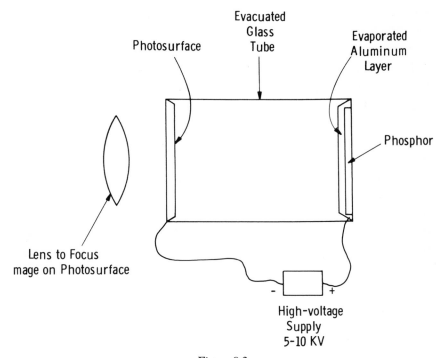

Figure 9.2

is a layer of photoelectric material; this is usually called a *photosurface*. On the inside of the other end-plate there is a phosphor layer. Electrical connections must be made to both these layers. This is simple for the photosurface, because practical photoemitters are reasonably good electrical conductors as a rule; phosphors, on the other hand, are usually electrical insulators, and therefore a thin layer of aluminum is evaporated onto the back of the phosphor to make electrical connection. This layer must not be too thick, because electrons have to pass through it on their way to the phosphor. Finally, a high direct voltage—perhaps five to ten thousand volts—is applied between the two connections, making the phosphor positive in relation to the photosurface. The tube is now ready for operation.

Let's suppose that by using a lens system an image of an illuminated scene is focused on the photosurface, just as the lens of a camera focuses an image on the film. The photosurface will then emit electrons, the intensity or rate of emission varying across the photosurface in correspondence with the light intensity in different areas of the image. These electrons, accelerated by the electric field between the photosurface and phosphor, travel along the electric field lines toward the phosphor. When they strike the phosphor, they cause it to fluoresce with an intensity that varies with position in correspondence with the electron density. A replica of the image at the photosurface is therefore produced at the phosphor by the fluorescence. Thus, an optical image is converted into an electronic one, then back to optical again.

Of what use is such a roundabout process? Why not look at the original image directly, as we would through a telescope? There are two immediate classes of answers. First, because the photosurface can be made sensitive to light of wavelengths somewhat too long for the eye to see (that is, infrared) while the phosphor fluoresces in the visible, an invisible infrared image can be converted into a visible optical one. This enables us to see in the dark, using an infrared light source, and it is the basis for the well-known "Snooperscope" used for military night-vision in World War II. The other kind of answer is dependent on our previous statement that for roughly each ten quanta incident on the photosurface, we can expect one photoelectron which in turn will yield about fifty quanta at the phosphor. The device thus yields an output image five times brighter than the input image, and this makes it possible to view scenes too dim for direct vision. Such a device is usually called an *image intensifier.*

As we have just described it, the intensifier suffers from a very serious defect whose description will introduce the fascinating field of electron optics. The difficulty lies in the fact that the electrons do not emerge from the photosurface with zero velocity, but in general have an initial velocity that varies between zero and that corresponding to the incident light quantum energy in excess of the work function, as described before. Furthermore, these velocities are in random directions; in consequence, a group of electrons that all originate at a given point on the photosurface do not all fall on the same point of the phosphor—a sharp point of light focused on the photosurface produces a broader, fuzzier spot on the phosphor. This results in a loss of fine detail in the output picture. The ability of the tube, or of

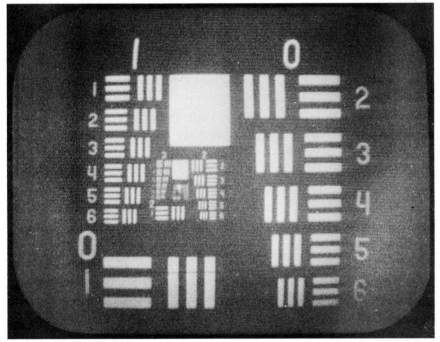

(Westinghouse Research Laboratory)

A resolution test pattern as seen through the type of image tube called the Secondary-Electron-Conduction Vidicon. The largest bars are one-half millimeter wide and are spaced one-half millimeter apart; each subgroup of six sets of bars spans a factor of two in geometric progression.

the complete system, to preserve such fine detail is quantitatively specified by the *resolution* of the system. This is the maximum number of alternate equal-width black and white bars per unit length in the input image whose replica can be seen at the output. Typically, for a good image intensifier this is roughly thirty line pairs per millimeter.

However, this figure would probably be less than one line pair per millimeter for the tube we have described, because the electrons are spread by their randomly directed initial velocities. What we would like is some scheme that would make all electrons from a point on the photosurface converge to a single point on the phosphor, regardless of their initial energy. Our discussion of the cyclotron provides a clue to how this can be done. Let's assume that the tube is placed in a uniform magnetic field whose direction is parallel to the axis of the tube. Now the initial velocity of an electron from the photosurface may be considered the sum of two component velocities, one parallel to the direction of the magnetic (and the electric) field, the other perpendicular to this, as shown in Fig. 9.3. Since the electric field exerts a force on the electron only in the direction of the field, that is, parallel to the axis of the tube, it can never affect the perpendicular component of velocity, only the parallel one. Furthermore, since a magnetic field, as we have seen, can exert a force on an electron only in a direction perpendicular to both its own direction and the direction of the electron motion, the magnetic field can never affect the motion along the axis of the tube but only motion in the perpen-

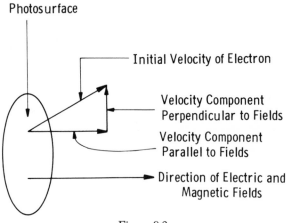

Figure 9.3

dicular direction. Thus, we can consider the motions of the electron in the parallel and the perpendicular direction independently, and combine these later to obtain a complete picture.

In the direction parallel to the fields, the story is quite simple. The electric field, and therefore the force on the electron and the resultant acceleration, are constant everywhere, which means that the electron's velocity along the field increases uniformly with time. Because there are several thousand volts between the phosphor and the photosurface, while the initial velocity of the electron corresponds to about one volt, we can in this case neglect the parallel component of the initial velocity. Then all photoelectrons will undergo the same acceleration, have the same parallel velocity, and travel from photosurface to phosphor in an equal transit time, and this incidentally is given by

$$t = \frac{3.38 \times 10^{-8}\, d}{\sqrt{v_1} + \sqrt{v_2}},$$

where t is in seconds, d is the photosurface-to-phosphor distance in centimeters, and v_1 and v_2 are the initial and the final energies of the electron in electron-volts.

As with the cyclotron, the motion perpendicular to the field is circular. Referring to Eq. 9.3 again, we concluded that although the size of the circular orbit of the proton depended on its energy, the time to complete an orbit did not. Similarly, the perpendicular motion of the electron in the tube is a circular orbit whose size depends on the initial perpendicular component of velocity, but whose period—time per complete revolution—is independent of initial veloctiy. Thus, considering only the perpendicular motion, all electrons from a point on the photosurface describe circles whose radii and centers depend on the individual electron's initial velocity; but at the end of one revolution, all these electrons arrive simultaneously again at their point of origin, and then repeat the procedure.

When this circular motion is superimposed on the uniform axial acceleration provided by the electric field, it is evident that these circular orbits are stretched along the tube's axis into a helix or corkscrew whose axis is parallel to that of the tube. (Since the electron is gaining velocity, the spacing of the turns is non-uniform.) The important point here is that after one revolution (or any whole number) all electrons from a given point will arrive simultaneously at a common point on the magnetic field line, and on the electric field line, which passes through their point of origin.

If we now choose the relative values of magnetic field and applied voltage so that the transit time from photosurface to phosphor is an integer times the time for one revolution, then all electrons from a point on the photosurface will initially diverge, describing helices of various sizes en route to the phosphor. But as they strike the phosphor they will all converge to a common point. This point, of course, lies on the same magnetic and electric field line as that of origin. By this means we have reduced the fuzzy spot on the phosphor to a sharp point, thereby vastly improving the clarity and resolution of the output image.

This process is called electron focusing, in analogy to the similar process of optical focusing; the general field of analysis of the paths of electrons in arbitrary electric and magnetic fields, in similar analogy, is known as electron optics. The problem we have just been discussing is a particularly simple one because since the magnetic and electric fields are uniform and parallel, the parallel and perpendicular motions are independent. It will be appreciated that to achieve this, special care is usually required in shaping the fields. It is also possible to make electron imaging systems using only electric fields of suitable shape, necessarily non-uniform. These are advantageous in eliminating the size and weight of the solenoid or permanent magnet required for magnetic fields. However, purely electric systems are usually somewhat inferior in resolution to those using magnetic fields as well.

A brightness gain of only five, while useful, is nonetheless disappointingly low. To increase this figure, we turn to the phenomenon of secondary electron emission. Since we have already noted that electrons can be freed from materials by light quanta, we should not be surprised to find that the same result can also occur by the impact of energetic electrons. As in fluorescence, the incident *primary* electrons lose their energy in a series of collisions; in each collision some energy is given up to the other electrons in the material. The average energy transfer may readily exceed the work function of the material, and in this case some of these *secondary* electrons may escape from the material entirely. The average number of secondary electrons produced by a primary electron of given energy in a given

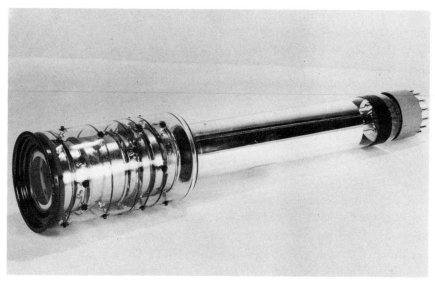

(Westinghouse Research Laboratory)

The Secondary-Electron-Conduction Vidicon, which employs the potassium chloride smoke dynodes described in the text. Both secondary electron emission from the dynodes and conduction by secondary electrons within the dynode are utilized.

material is called the *secondary emission coefficient.* This number is frequently greater than one; for many solids it is of the order of six to eight, while for some materials in the form of smoke deposits it is as much as fifty to one hundred. An important consideration is the stability, or constancy with time, of this number. Quite stable values exceeding fifty can now be achieved.

If the primary electrons fall on a relatively thick material (thicker than, say, 0.01 mm), secondaries will emerge only from the surface struck by the primaries; this is usually called *reflection secondary emission.* If, however, a sufficiently thin film of material is used, appreciable secondary emission occurs from the surface opposite to that struck by the primaries. Again, stable ratios as high as fifty are possible. This process, called *transmission secondary emission,* can be advantageously used in the image tube in the following way. Somewhere, roughly midway between photosurface and phosphor, is placed a thin-film secondary emitter deposited on a thin aluminum film, the latter for support and electrical conductivity. The aluminum side faces the photosurface and is electrically connected to a potential between that of photosurface and phosphor. The electrons from the photosurface now must form an image on the aluminum-backed secondary emitter, just as they previously did on the phosphor; but for every photoelectron striking the film, as many as fifty secondary electrons emerge from a very small area on the opposite face. Of course, these proceed to the phosphor, where they are focused to form an image that is now not five but two hundred and fifty times brighter than the original. The focusing conditions are therefore more stringent, since they must be satisfied in two regions simultaneously, but this is readily done. Because the film is quite thin, the secondaries due to a single primary emerge from a small area and thus rather good resolution can still be obtained in addition to brightness gain. Indeed, several successive films—as many as five—have been employed in cascade, as shown in Fig. 9.4. However, these were solid films rather than smoke deposits, resulting in an overall gain of about 250,000. This figure could probably be attained with only three smoke-deposit films.

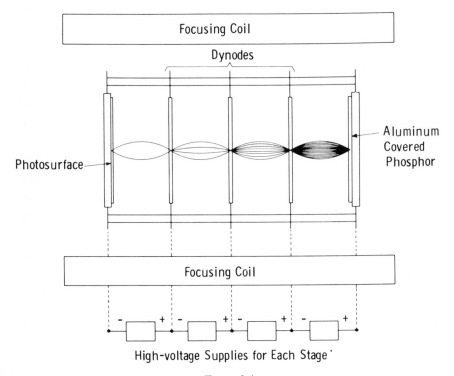

Figure 9.4

Secondary-emission image intensifiers have been applied with great success to many problems of low-light-level viewing, including astronomy, x-ray crystallography, night viewing, cosmic ray observation, and high-speed photography. Sensitivity can be made great enough so that single photoelectrons produce visible flashes of light at the output. This is clearly about as high a sensitivity as can be useful.

The study of light has always been a source of mystery, fascination, and delight. The history of man's efforts to fathom the nature of light is well known—first the corpuscular theory, then the wave theory, and now quantum theory have brought us far in our ability to understand light, to produce it, and to employ it as a scientific tool. In this final section of our book, we will discuss an important recent development in modern optics, the *laser*. The name is an acronym, the initials of Light Amplification by Stimulated Emission of Radiation.

The answer to the ancient question of whether light "is" a wave or a particle (if, indeed, it is either) usually depends on the particular circumstances in which the question is asked. At relatively intense light levels, for instance, it is frequently—although not always—adequate to describe light as an electromagnetic wave whose behavior is completely specified by Maxwell's famous set of four equations. In cases of very low light level, however, it is usually necessary to recognize the the energy of light is packaged, as we have seen, in individual bundles or quanta, and that when this energy enters into physical processes the entire energy of a quantum is always involved as a unit— never is just part of a quantum produced or consumed. In regard to this indivisibility, quanta show some aspects of particles. The reason this behavior can often be ignored at high light levels is that the measurements we make usually concern averages of so many light quanta that the discreteness of a quantum makes only negligible percentage difference in the calculations. However, in cases involving only a few quanta, the impossibility of fractional values of energy may make a great difference. Just so is the granularity of sand negligible in weighing a truckload, but all-important when a single grain is lodged in one's eye. Perhaps the most satisfactory way to state the case is to say that light energy occurs in discrete, indivisible bundles called quanta, and although the propagational behavior of a single quantum cannot be accurately predicted, the *average* propagation of a large number of quanta is accurately described by Maxwell's equation of electromagnetic wave motion. A similar situation exists in games of chance, where the outcome of a single game is unpredictable, but the average outcome of many repetitions of the game can be calculated in advance.

The production of light is intimately connected with the structure of matter. As we have already mentioned, the energies permitted electrons in matter are restricted to certain specified values, characteristic of the material. These values, however, are in principle not specified with absolute precision but are subject to a small indeterminacy, often called the *sharpness* of the energy state. A further restriction is that an energy level may be filled or empty—that is, there may or may not be an electron which at the moment actually has that energy—but no level may be occupied by more than one electron at a time. This situation is somewhat analogous to that of seats in a theater.

Concerning the distribution of these states with respect to their energy, nearly always in isolated or widely separated molecules (for example, in gases), the energy levels are discrete and separated; for each allowed level it is possible to specify a small but finite range of energy larger than the level's sharpness in which only this level, and no other allowed levels, occurs. In solids, frequently the allowed levels in certain energy ranges are so densely packed that they are separated from each other by less than their sharpness. In this case, individual levels lose much of their meaning, and the range of energy becomes a permitted band. The discreteness of the levels is still significant, however, in that the band may never be occupied by more electrons than the number of levels of which it is composed.

When an electron makes a transition from one allowed level to another—which necessarily is unoccupied—it obviously must gain or lose an amount of energy equal to the difference between these levels. Such a gain in energy may come, for example, from absorption of a suitable light quantum, from the absorbed energy of an impinging electron, or from energy furnished by thermal motion. Likewise, a loss of energy may result in the emission of a light quantum, or in the transfer of energy to another electron, or the evolution of heat. The absorption or production of light is accomplished only by such electronic transitions. Thus, the generation of light requires empty (unfilled) electron energy levels, and occupied levels of higher energy above these, from which the electrons can make transition to the empty levels.

We have already described some of the many ways this can be done. In an incandescent bulb, the filament is electrically heated sufficiently for thermal energy to raise some electrons to higher-energy excited states from which light-emitting transitions occur. As another example, in a semiconductor *P-N* junction with forward applied voltage, some of the carriers that cross the junction can recombine with majority carriers. In other words, the electron makes a transition from its original energy level to that of the hole, and in doing this it emits a quantum of light. This process is called *injection electroluminescence.* There are some restrictions on the transitions permitted which are equivalent to the requirements of conservation of both energy and momentum, mentioned in the discussion of electron-hole recombination in Chapter Seven. Because of these restrictions, this process is significant only in semiconductors such as gallium arsenide. We have already discussed a third way to produce light, and this utilizes electron bombardment of a phosphor to raise electrons to excited energy levels from which they return to their original states by light-emitting transitions.

A characteristic of all the processes mentioned so far is that the downward transitions almost all occur independently and randomly. Each excited electron stays in its excited state for a rather short time which fluctuates about an average value that depends on the nature of the particular state; it then reverts to its ground state at some randomly chosen instant. Thus, the starting time—and therefore the phase—of the electromagnetic waves associated with each quantum are unrelated. The resulting radiation is said to be *incoherent,* since its quanta are random in phase relation.

However, there is a probability, small but finite, that the electromagnetic wave associated with a particular quantum produced by a downward transition may affect another electron in an excited state, causing it to fall to its lower state as the wave passes it, and to emit a quantum whose electromagnetic wave is precisely in phase, or *coherent,* with that of the first quantum. This effect is called *stimulated* or *induced emission,* and it may be thought of as analogous to chemical catalysis, in that the first quantum is not consumed or absorbed but

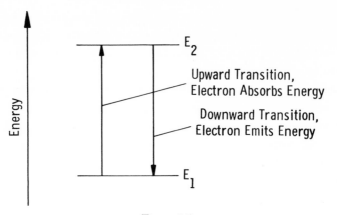

Figure 9.5

merely acts as a trigger for the release of the second. It is alternatively possible, of course, that the original quantum will induce an electron in a lower energy state to make a transition to an upper state, and in this case the original quantum is entirely absorbed. Now, let's consider a simplified system in which only two energy states are possible, as indicated in Fig. 9.5. Some of the electrons, let's say, have been raised to the upper state by one of the processes previously discussed. Then a light quantum produced from a downward transition might escape entirely from the material, might induce further emission by an upper-state electron, or might be absorbed in inducing a lower-state electron to transfer into the upper state. It can be shown that the probability per unit time that a given upper-state electron will be induced to emit is equal to that of a given lower-state electron being induced to absorb. In conventional light-generating processes these probabilities are small compared to the probability that an upper-state electron will spontaneously fall (regardless of any external cause) to the lower state, and thereby emit. Thus, nearly all the light quanta are emitted independently and with random phases.

The laser utilizes the coherence of induced emission to provide a light source in which the electromagnetic waves of all the emitted quanta are in phase. It does this by using a material whose energy levels are such that the probability of spontaneous emission is small compared to that of stimulated emission, so that the only significant emission is that stimulated by an initial quantum. The electromagnetic field of this initial quantum, traversing the material (usually many times by means of multiple reflections) will be reinforced by the emission it stimulates, thus building up a wave of large amplitude which emerges from the material as a beam of highly parallel coherent light.

In order to have such a build-up, it is clearly necessary that on the whole there be more stimulated emission than absorption. Since the probabilities of each are equal, in the sense previously described, it is obvious that a net build-up occurs only if there are more electrons in the upper energy state than in the lower. Such a situation is not trivial to produce. Obviously it is not one of thermodynamic equilibrium, because the population of a state in equilibrium always decreases as its energy increases. Thus, the desired population, called an *inverted* population, cannot be produced by heating, for example. It is necessary to find some means of raising electrons from the lower to the upper state at a rate high compared to the spontaneous-emission rate at which they return to the lower level.

Of several possible techniques, one employs the use of a system in which there are not two but three permitted energy levels, as shown diagrammatically in Fig. 9.6. From the normal ground state E_1, electrons are excited to state E_2, for instance, by irradiation with light whose quanta are of energy $E_2 - E_1$, or whose frequency is $\nu = \dfrac{E_2 - E_1}{h}$.
The electrons raised to state E_2 will be subject to both induced emission to state E_1 and spontaneous emission to both states E_1 and E_3. However, the rate of induced emission is proportional to the in-

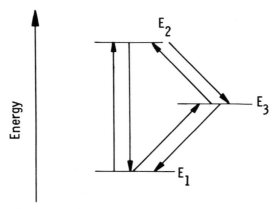

Figure 9.6

tensity of the irradiating light, and if this is made sufficiently intense the rate of spontaneous emission can be ignored. Now, the total rate at which electrons can be excited from state E_1 is proportional to the product $B_{12}N_1$, where B_{12} is the probability of an individual electron being excited, and N_1 is the number of electrons in state E_1. Similarly, the total rate of de-excitation from state E_2 is proportional to $B_{21}N_2$, with corresponding definitions. The net rate at which the population of state E_2 changes must then be proportional to the difference between these two quantities, or to $B_{12}N_1 - B_{21}N_2$. In steady state, by definition, this must be zero; since we have already said that B_{12} and B_{21} are equal, this requires that N_1 equal N_2. Before radiation was applied, the ratio of the original equilibrium populations of these states, which we might call N_{1e} and N_{2e}, depended exponentially on the energy difference between the states:

$$N_{2e} = N_{1e} \, \varepsilon^{-(E_2-E_1)/kT},$$

so that N_{2e} is less (very much less in a typical case) than N_{1e}. Similar relationships hold for the population of state E_3.

On application of radiation, N_2 is increased at the depletion of N_1, and since the population of state E_3 is not directly affected, the sum of N_1 and N_2 must not be changed by the radiation, so evidently,

$$N_1 = N_2 = \tfrac{1}{2}\,(N_{1e} + N_{2e}) = \tfrac{1}{2}\,N_{1e}\,(1 + \varepsilon^{-(E_2-E_1)/kT}).$$

Thus, the population N_2 is now more than half of N_{1e}. If N_3 (which will be nearly its equilibrium value, $N_{3e} = N_{1e}\,\varepsilon^{-(E_2-E_1)/kT}$) is less than this, a condition easily assured by making $\varepsilon^{-(E_3-E_1)/kT} < \tfrac{1}{2}$, which requires only that $E_3 - E_1 > 0.7\,kT$, then we will have achieved a population inversion of state E_2 over state E_3. If now light of quantum energy $E_2 - E_3$ enters the system, there will be more stimulated emission than absorption, thus augmenting the original wave and resulting in a plane wave (that is, a wave of parallel light) of much greater intensity than the original.

Let's compare the function of this device to that of the more familiar electronic systems—those used in radio, for example. Apparently the laser can act as an amplifier, for the light output is greater than, but proportional to, the input. The ratio of output to input, the gain or amplification of the system, can be increased by positive feedback. In the conventional electronic amplifier this is done by return-

(Westinghouse Research Laboratory)

A laser beam makes a pyrotechnic display as it vaporizes a hole through a thin aluminum sheet.

ing a part of the output to the input circuit. Clearly, less input is then required for a given output, so that the gain has been increased. In the case of the laser, this feedback is accomplished by mirrors which reflect part of the output light back into the material, resulting in increased gain. The laser behaves like a tuned amplifier in that the gain is high only at or near a specific frequency, that corresponding to the energy difference $E_2 - E_3$. If the feedback is made sufficient, all of the input required for a given output may be obtained from the output itself. In this case, just as with the electronic system, the gain is infinite, and the laser becomes an optical oscillator, a source of sinusoidal energy. As with the vacuum-tube oscillator or other electronic systems, this optical energy output must be derived from an auxiliary energy supply. In the electronic system, this source is the direct-current supply which provides vacuum-tube anode voltage, transistor collector voltage, or its equivalent; in the laser, it is the source of "pumping" light which excites electrons from state E_1 to state E_2. One may speak of the efficiency of an oscillator as the fraction of the input energy which is converted to output energy. For a transistor or vacuum-tube system, this figure can approach 100 percent, but for lasers it is much lower, typically 0.1 percent. This in no way detracts from the usefulness of the laser as an amplifier. It has, on the other hand, the advantage of very low noise, for the entire system can be operated at liquid helium temperatures where thermal agitation, the chief contributor to laser noise, is very small. Such systems constitute the lowest-noise (and hence most sensitive) microwave amplifiers known today. When operated in the microwave region—as historically occurred first—rather than at optical frequencies, the device is called a *maser* (*m* for microwave). Masers have been used very successfully in many applications, among them radio astronomy, microwave radar, and atomic clocks.

In ending a book such as this, there is always a temptation to gaze into the crystal ball, extrapolating predictions of what may come about twenty or fifty years from now. We hasten to admit that our crystal ball is no better than most; doubtless this is fortunate, for where then would be the enjoyment of prediction? Perhaps as instructive a guide to the future as any is a brief look at the past. The secondary-emission image tube and the transistor were unknown barely fifteen years ago, and high-energy accelerators were in their infancy. The forerunners of modern electronic computers had just begun to be constructed. Vacuum tubes have been known only about fifty years, and quantum theory and relativity themselves are products of this century. In this connection it should be pointed out, however, that the fundamental equations describing the electromagnetic fields produced by electric charge have stood unchanged since their publication by James Clerk Maxwell in 1873.

What, then, may we expect next? On the side of theory, one perplexing aspect of present-day high-energy physics is that a bewildering host of "fundamental" particles has appeared in the last one or two decades, with no really satisfying way of consistently categorizing their properties. One has the feeling that nature should actually not be so complicated. But recently there has developed some indication that most—or perhaps, indeed, all—of these particles may be identifiable as various energy states of a single closely associated combination of a few electrons and positrons. Such an identification, at present speculative, might go far to simplify the state of elementary-particle physics. In the physics of solids, new information pours forth continuously from studies conducted by maser techniques on the energy states of impurity atoms in solids. These will surely result in more lucid understanding of the properties of solids, and of better ways to use these properties. Improved semiconductor devices of ever higher power and frequency, or smaller size, are legion, and significant progress has been made in controlling the flow of electric current in solid-state devices employing not semiconductors but thin layers of metal and metal oxides. These may eventually offer higher-temperature and higher-frequency operation than their semiconductor counterparts.

Sometime within the next decade it is very probable that man will reach the moon—and not long thereafter, at least the nearer planets. It is rather likely that his ship will be guided by a solid-state electronic computer, and that its eyes and ears may be electronic image tubes and maser or laser communications systems. It is even possible that part of its propulsion may be furnished by particle accelerators or magnetohydrodynamic systems acting as ion rockets. How far man will go, or in what direction, only time can tell. But whether at home or afar, his machines and his life will surely be vitally dependent on electrons on the move.

Appendix

Certain Symbols

A	α	alpha	I	ι	iota	P	ρ	rho
B	β	beta	K	κ	kappa	Σ	σ	sigma
Γ	γ	gamma	Λ	λ	lambda	T	τ	tau
Δ	δ	delta	M	μ	mu	Υ	υ	upsilon
E	ε	epsilon	N	ν	nu	Φ	φ	phi
Z	ζ	zeta	Ξ	ξ	xi	X	χ	chi
H	η	eta	O	o	omicron	Ψ	ψ	psi
Θ	θ	theta	Π	π	pi	Ω	ω	omega

In scientific notation, it has become customary to use certain symbols, as well as Greek and Roman letters, to denote specific quantities. Throughout this book such symbols have been defined in context, but the following list, intended only for reference, gives commonly accepted definitions of the letters and symbols most frequently encountered.

Δ	finite difference	H	magnetic field intensity
θ, φ, ψ	angle	h	Planck's constant
φ	work function	i, I	electric current
λ	wavelength	k	Boltzmann's constant
ν	frequency	l, L	length
ρ	density, or resistivity	m, M	mass
ω	angular velocity	n, N	number, especially
c	velocity of light		an integer
d	distance	P	pressure
E	energy, or electric field	p	momentum
e	charge of the electron, or the base of the natural logarithms	q, Q	amount of charge
		R	universal gas constant
		r	radius
F	force	T	temperature
f	frequency	t	time
G	gravitation constant	v, V	velocity, volume, voltage
g	acceleration of gravity	∞	infinity

Certain Scientists

ANAXAGORAS (500 B.C.–428 B.C.) Greek philosopher and teacher, exiled for introducing an explanation of the universe which included the theory that all matter derives from a chaotic mass of small particles or "seeds." This part of his concept is fundamental to the atomic theory.

AVOGADRO, Count Amadeo (1776–1856) Italian physicist and chemist, who suggested in 1811 the principle that equal volumes of all gases at the same temperature contain identical numbers of molecules. Avogadro's law was much later elucidated by the Maxwell-Boltzmann law of equipartition of energy, and positively established by the experiments of J. J. Thomson, Millikan, Rutherford, and others. Avogadro's Constant is the number of molecules contained in one mole (gram-molecular weight) of a substance.

BOLTZMANN, Ludwig (1844–1906) Austrian physicist, who is known especially for the Stefan-Boltzmann law of black-body radiation. Boltzmann contributed to the probability theory and the partition of energy in connection with the kinetic theory of gases.

CAVENDISH, Henry (1731–1810) English chemist and physicist. Cavendish discovered nitric acid, and by inductive experiments combined oxygen and hydrogen into water. He also anticipated a number of later discoveries concerning the nature of electricity.

CLASSEN, Alexander (1843–1934) German chemist, who did important and extensive work in analytical chemistry, particularly electrochemistry. His numerous textbooks have been widely translated.

CLAUSIUS, Rudolf Julius Emanuel (1822–1880) German physicist, noted for his work in thermodynamics, and especially for his formulation of the second law of thermodynamics in 1850. He also introduced the concept of entropy, and contributed to the kinetic theory of gases, as well as to the theory of electrolysis.

COCKROFT, Sir John Douglas (1897–   ) English physicist, who at one time worked with Ernest Walton as Ernest Rutherford's assistant. In 1951 he shared the Nobel prize in physics with Walton for their pioneering work with atomic nuclei.

COULOMB, Charles Augustin de (1736–1806) French physicist, noted for his experiments on friction and for his researches in electricity and magnetism. He formulated Coulomb's law of the forces existing between charged bodies, and the coulomb, a unit of electrical quantity, is named for him.

CROOKES, Sir William (1832–1919) English physicist and chemist. As early as 1886, Crookes contended that elements contain atoms of different atomic weights, and he devised a spiral model of the periodic system. His pioneer studies in rarefied gases led to his observing the dark space which bears his name.

DAVISSON, Clinton Joseph (1881–   ) American physicist, known for his research work in electricity, magnetism, and radiant energy. In 1927, he and Lester Germer discovered the diffraction of electrons by crystals, for which he shared the 1937 Nobel prize with the English physicist George Paget Thomson, who had discovered the same phenomenon independently and by a different method.

DAVY, Sir Humphry (1778–1829) English scientist. While professor of chemistry at the Royal Institute, London, he first isolated several of the elements by electrolysis. Noted for his demonstration that diamond is a carbon, he is probably even better known as the inventor of a safety lamp used in mines.

DEMOCRITUS (460 B.C.–357 B.C.) Greek philosopher, who expanded the atomistic theory of Leucippus. Only fragments of his written works in which he expounded this theory have survived.

DIRAC, Paul Adrien Maurice (1902–   ) British mathematical physicist in the field of atomic structure. In 1933 Dirac was awarded the Nobel prize (jointly with Erwin Schrödinger) for his pioneer work in the quantum mechanics of the atom. He was co-discoverer of the Fermi-Dirac statistics, and also pioneered in developing the quantum theory of radiation.

FARADAY, Michael (1791–1867) English physicist and chemist, whose greatest contributions were in the fields of electricity and magnetism. His discoveries of electromagnetic induction, the magnetization of light, and diamagnetism are especially noteworthy. He was also responsible for advances in the study of electrolysis, the liquefaction of gases, and many other areas of physics and chemistry.

GAY-LUSSAC, Joseph Louis (1778–1850) French chemist and physicist, noted for his researches on chemical combinations, iodine, and cyanogen. He enunciated the law that bears his name, stating that gases combine with each other in simple definite proportions.

GEISSLER, Heinrich (1814–1879) German mechanic, who invented Geissler's tubes, in which light is produced by an electric discharge through rarefied gases.

GERMER, Lester H. (1896–   ) American physicist, noted for his researches in thermionics, electron diffraction, and metal erosion, as well as for his work in contact physics and surface physics. In 1927, Germer and Clinton Davisson discovered the diffraction of electrons by crystals.

GIESE, Wilhelm (1847–   ) In Berlin in 1882 Herr Giese put forward the theory of conduction through gases stating that conducting gases contain positively and negatively charged ions or particles. He applied this theory to the explanation of the electrical conductivity of the gases from a flame.

GOLDSTEIN, Eugen (1850–1930) German physicist who discovered canal rays. He is noted for his studies of cathode rays, especially in electrostatic diversion.

HAUKSBEE, Francis (–1713) English experimenter, who in 1706 created a light-producing electrical apparatus which he called the light "mechanical phosphorus." Hauksbee also contributed to improvement of the air pump design, and determined quite exact relative weights of air and water.

HAYNES, J. Richard (1901–) American physicist, who developed the carbon microphone and spark gap tubes for radar modulators. His researches at Bell Telephone Laboratories have been in the areas of solid-state physics, transistor physics, and recombination radiation of semiconductors.

HEAVISIDE, Oliver (1850–1925) Self-trained English electrician and mathematical physicist, a disciple of Faraday and Maxwell. In 1902, Heaviside suggested the existence of an atmospheric layer having special properties, dependent on the wavelength, in the propagation of radio waves; this is now known as the Heaviside layer.

HEISENBERG, Werner (1901–) German physicist whose matrix theory of quantum mechanics is an important factor in the general quantum theory. He was awarded the 1932 Nobel prize in physics for this contribution and for his investigations of hydrogen.

HELMHOLTZ, Hermann Ludwig Ferdinand (1821–1894) German physiologist and physicist, especially noted for his discoveries in optics and acoustics. Helmholtz invented the ophthalmoscope and made outstanding contributions to both physiology and physical theory.

HERTZ, Heinrich (1857–1894) German physicist, known especially for his discovery of the electric waves of large amplitude which have been utilized in wireless telegraphy. He also did significant investigation of the relation between electricity and light, and the properties of electrical discharges in rarefied gases.

HITTORF, Johann Wilhelm (1824–1914) German physicist, who pioneered in the study of cathode rays. His researches in the migration of ions during electrolysis and his measurements of relative velocities of different ions pulled through water by an electric field led to later ionic theories.

JEFFREYS, Sir Harold (1891–) British mathematician and professor of astronomy. Jeffreys is the author of numerous scientific papers and books, among them "The Earth, Its Origin, History and Physical Constitution," "Methods of Mathematical Physics," and "Theory of Probability."

KAUFMANN, Walther (1871–   ) In 1901 he demonstrated that the mass of electrons increases as the velocity approaches that of light. Earlier in 1897 he devised a method for estimating the ratio e/m for cathode rays at the same time that Wiechert and Thomson were working on the problem.

KELVIN, Lord (William Thomson) (1824–1907) British physicist, born in Ireland. Kelvin was recognized as one of the greatest physicists of his time. Influenced by Joule's theory of heat, he proposed an absolute scale of temperature independent of any thermometric substance. A few years later, Kelvin reconciled the work of Sadi Carnot with that of Count Rumford, Sir Humphry Davy, J. R. Mayer, and Joule; his resulting dynamical theory of heat and the fundamental principle of conservation of energy commanded universal acceptance. At the same time he first stated briefly his principle of dissipation of energy, the second law of thermodynamics. Kelvin's contributions to thermodynamics are considered of primary importance, but he was also responsible for significant advances in many other areas of research.

LAWRENCE, Ernest Orlando (1901–1958) American physicist who invented the cyclotron in 1930. Lawrence, professor of physics and director of the radiation laboratory of the University of California, did notable work on the structure of atoms and of the atomic nucleus, effected transmutation of certain elements, and produced artificial radioactivity. He applied his experimental results to problems of physics and biology. His outstanding contribution was recognized by his being awarded the Nobel prize for physics in 1939.

LENARD, Phillip (1862–1947) German physicist, who received the Nobel prize in 1905 for his significant work on cathode rays. Lenard demonstrated that light causes the emission of electrons from substances, and that the velocity of emission is not related to the light intensity but that the frequency of light affects the velocity. He also helped modify Thomson's early picture of the structure of the atom, indicating that it is mostly empty space through which many electrons pass without colliding with other electrons or with the nucleus. The Lenard rays in a Crooke's tube are named for him.

MAXWELL, James Clerk (1831–1879) British physicist, born in Scotland. At the age of fifteen, Maxwell made the first of his many scientific contributions, and by the time he was eighteen his singular genius was becoming apparent. In his extraordinary investigations, which included electricity, magnetism, elastic solids, color perception, and the kinetic theory of gases, Maxwell was not only the experimenter but often the mathematician as well. Of his many great contributions, the most significant dealt with the physical theory of electromagnetism.

MILLIKAN, Robert Andrews (1868–1953) American physicist, whose first outstanding contribution was his famous oil drop experiment, an accurate measurement of the charge of the electron, and proof that this charge is a definite quantity and therefore a fundamental constant. He later provided equally skillful experimental verification of Einstein's photoelectric equation, and the evaluation of Planck's constant. Millikan's researches also dealt with cosmic rays, the mysterious radiation from outer space. In 1923, he was awarded the Nobel prize in physics.

NEWTON, Sir Isaac (1642–1727) English mathematician and natural philosopher. There is no greater example of achievement in the history of science than that of Newton, who at twenty-three made three fundamental discoveries: the method of calculus, which is the basis for much of modern mathematics; the spectral composition of light and the fundamentals of optics; and the law of universal gravitation and the basic laws of mechanics.

OHM, Georg Simon (1787–1854) German physicist, especially noted for his investigations in electricity. Ohm, for whom the unit of electrical resistance, the ohm, is named, discovered the proportionality between an electric current flowing in a conductor and the electromotive force applied to it; this is known as "Ohm's law."

PERRIN, Jean Baptiste (1870–1942) French physicist and chemist, who was awarded the Nobel prize in physics in 1926 in recognition for his work on the discontinous structure of matter and for discovering the equilibrium of sedimentation. Perrin made notable investigations in light, electricity, and molecular physics, particularly the Brownian movement. His studies also included x rays, cathode rays, and electrons.

PLANCK, Max (1857–1947) German theoretical physicist, who made the significant discovery that energy exists in quantized form. From this premise, he derived the universal Law of Radiation in 1901. Professor of physics at Kiel and at Berlin, Planck was the author of such classic works on theoretical physics as "Theory of Heat Radiation." In 1918, he was awarded the Nobel prize in physics.

PLÜCKER, Julius (1801–1868) German mathematician and scientist, considered by many to have been the greatest analytical geometer of all time. Plücker devoted most of the last twenty years of his life to researches in magnetism, crystallography, and spectrum analysis.

ROWLAND, Henry Augustus (1848–1901) American physicist. Rowland was the first professor of physics at Johns Hopkins University, and the author of numerous papers on optics and electricity. He is particularly noted for his work on the solar spectrum. Rowland also remeasured the ohm, and redetermined the mechanical equivalent of heat.

SCHRÖDINGER, Erwin (1887–   ) German physicist, noted for having introduced wave mechanics, an advanced form of quantum theory, which made it possible to compute parameters and physical characteristics of the atom. He won the Nobel prize with Paul Dirac in 1933.

SCHUSTER, Sir Arthur (1851–1934) In 1890, Schuster measured the ratio of charge to mass for hypothetical negatively charged particles and found a value about five hundred times that of the same ratio for the hydrogen ion in electrolysis.

SHOCKLEY, William Bradford (1910–   ) American scientist, primarily noted for his outstanding work on transistors and semiconductors. The author of many scientific papers, as well as the book "Electrons and Holes in Semiconductors," Shockley was awarded the 1956 Nobel prize for his contributions in physics.

STOKES, Sir George Gabriel (1819–1903) British mathematician and physicist, professor of physics at Cambridge, who discovered the law that fluorescent light is shifted toward the red with respect to the primary radiation. Stokes was also the discoverer of the relation between the force and the velocity of bodies moving in fluids.

STONEY, George Johnston (1826–1911) Dr. Stoney was Irish and educated in Dublin. In 1891 he introduced the word, electron, to designate the elementary electrical charge. He computed the value of the electron by a method comparable in accuracy with any used up to 1909.

THOMSON, Sir Joseph John (1856–1940) British physicist who determined the ratio of mass and charge of the electron by the deflection of cathode rays in combined electric and magnetic fields.

VAN ALLEN, James Alfred (1914–   ) American physicist, who discovered the "Van Allen Belt" of radiation around the earth. He was a pioneer of high-altitude research and a founder of the International Academy of Astronautics.

VAN DE GRAAFF, Robert J. (1901–   ) American physicist, noted for having devised an electrostatic generator, which employs a system of conveyor belt and spray points to charge an insulated electrode to a high potential. This device is capable of accelerating charged particles to high enough energies to induce nuclear reactions.

VARLEY, Cromwell Fleetwood (1828–1883) Varley is known for developing an "influence machine," an electrostatic generator capable of producing very high voltages. This proved useful in long-distance power transmission. He also worked on the technical problems posed by the laying of the Atlantic cable. Varley's studies of alternating currents helped in the development of the telephone, and his work with the armature made it feasible to use the dynamo.

WALTON, Ernest Thomas Sinton (1903–   ) Irish physicist. Walton and John Cockroft, both assistants to Ernest Rutherford at one time, shared the 1951 Nobel prize in physics for their work in smashing atomic nuclei with electrically speeded atomic particles. Walton's investigations formed the basis for later development of the cyclotron and the entire atomic energy complex.

WATSON, Sir William (1715–1787) English physician and scientific experimenter, who developed a one-fluid electrical theory similar to that of Benjamin Franklin. In 1745, Watson was awarded the Copley medal for his electrical researches.

Wien, Wilhem (1864–1928) German physicist, who formulated a law of radiation later adapted by Einstein to the new situation created by Bohr's theory of spectra. Wien is especially noted for his research on the radiation of energy from black bodies, for which he was awarded the 1911 Nobel prize in physics.

Williamson, Alexander William (1824–1904) English chemist, professor at University College, London, from 1849 to 1887. Williamson is noted for his work on the constitution of the ether.

Wilson, Charles Thomson Rees (1869–1959) Scottish physicist and inventor of the Wilson cloud chamber, a means of making the paths of ions and atomic particles visible. His researches included atmospheric electricity, condensation nuclei, and ions. In 1927, Wilson shared the Nobel prize for physics with A. H. Compton.

The Authors

ALLAN BENNETT has been a staff member of the Westinghouse Research Laboratories since 1952, but his association with Westinghouse goes back to 1946, when he worked at the Laboratories for the first of several consecutive summers. He now holds the position of Advisory Physicist.

Dr. Bennett, who has spent most of his life so far in Western Pennsylvania, was born in Wilkinsburg and received his early education in Ligonier. After graduating from Pittsburgh's Shady Side Academy, he spent a year at Carnegie Institute of Technology before transferring to the U. S. Navy's V-12 program at Rensselaer Polytechnic Institute. In 1946 he received his Bachelor of Electrical Engineering degree and a naval reserve commission. When transferred to inactive duty, he returned to Carnegie Tech for graduate studies, receiving an M.S. in physics in 1948 and a Ph.D. in 1953. In the meantime he had married and the Bennetts now have three daughters and a son.

Although he claims that he simply can't remember a time when he was not determined on a scientific career, Dr. Bennett's interests embrace a broad range of activities—from swimming, skating, square dancing and photography, to duplicate bridge and electronic construction, particularly hi-fi systems. He is also in demand as a guitarist and ballad singer.

An enthusiastic teacher, Dr. Bennett is currently conducting an evening course in physics at Carnegie Tech, as well as teaching a third grade Sunday School class. He is also co-manager of the yearly Westinghouse science lectures for advanced high school students.

ROBERT HEIKES had just completed his graduate work at the University of Chicago and received his Ph.D. degree, when he joined the staff of the Westinghouse Research Laboratories in 1952. He is now Director of Solid State Sciences Research and Development.

A native Pennsylvanian, he was born in Millersburg and received his early education there. His interest in chemistry was nurtured by understanding parents who provided him with a home chemistry laboratory, which he now claims was "only slightly better equipped" than the one at his high school. With such encouragement, it is not surprising that he pursued his study of science at Massachusetts Institute of Technology, graduating with a Bachelor of Science degree.

Dr. Heikes, who was married the same year he came to Westinghouse, is the father of a nine-year-old daughter. Often accompanied by his family, he has traveled extensively in Europe, where he is in demand as a technical consultant, a lecturer, and a teacher. He enjoys foreign languages and speaks several, including Russian. The author of numerous technical articles and the co-author of the book *Thermoelectricity*, Dr. Heikes is presently writing a science textbook in French for French high school students.

Dr. Heikes and his wife, both active connoisseurs of rare wines and food, take turns in the kitchen perparing gourmet dinners for their friends; the souvenir menus are beautifully designed and enhanced by original French verse.

PAUL KLEMENS came to the United States from Australia in 1959 to join the staff of the Westinghouse Research Laboratories. He has since worked primarily on the theory of conduction properties of solids, and on other non-equilibrium processes. A skillful instructor and the author of more than seventy scientific papers, Dr. Klemens has recently returned from a year of teaching at the University of Leyden.

After receiving his Bachelor of Science and Master of Science degrees from the University of Sydney in Australia, he continued his studies at Oxford University in England. With a Ph.D. from Oxford, Dr. Klemens returned to Australia in 1950 and accepted a research position with the National Standards Laboratory in Sydney, where he remained until he came to this country.

When not absorbed in his scientific work or trying to cope with the demands of his two children, Dr. Klemens relaxes with his collection of rare stamps or delves into eighteenth century history. Although he claims that he is a rather indifferent sportsman, he enjoys tennis, swimming, and golf.

In explaining his choice of a career, Dr. Klemens says that when he was in high school his interest in mathematics stimulated his interest in science, particularly physics. He found that as a theoretical physicist he would be able to pursue both of these interests.

218

ALEXEI MARADUDIN was Assistant Research Professor at the University of Maryland when he was invited in 1960 to join the staff of the Westinghouse Research Laboratories. He is now an Advisory Physicist.

The son of a Russian metallurgist who came to this country following the revolution, Dr. Maradudin was born in San Francisco and grew up in the Los Angeles area. He entered Stanford University at the age of seventeen, and five years later graduated with great distinction, a Phi Beta Kappa key, and a Master of Science degree in physical metallurgy. In September of the same year, he married a classmate and took her to England, where he continued his graduate studies as a Marshall scholar. In 1956, he received a Ph.D. degree in physics from the University of Bristol.

The Maradudins, who now have a small son and an even smaller daughter, are enthusiastic participants in civic and church affairs. They also share an enthusiasm for literature, classical music, fine wines, and Persian cats.

Dr. Maradudin, the author of numerous scientific papers, articles, and books, lectures from time to time at various universities and has traveled widely in Europe in connection with his work. Recently this young American was invited to participate in a conference on Solid State Physics in Moscow. He spoke on *Lattice Dynamics*—in fluent Russian.

For Further Reading

PART ONE

Anderson, David L. *The Discovery of the Electron.* Princeton, N.J.: D. Van Nostrand Co., 1963.

Millikan, Robert Andrews. *The Electron: Its Isolation and Measurement and the Determination of Some of Its Properties.* Edited with an introduction by Jesse W. M. DuMond. Chicago: University of Chicago Press, 1963.

PART TWO

Harman, Willis W. *Fundamentals of Electronic Motion.* New York: McGraw-Hill Book Co., 1953.

Klemperer, Otto. *Electron Physics: The Physics of the Free Electron.* New York: Academic Press, 1959.

Lemon, Harvey Brace, Ference, Michael, Jr., and Stephenson, Reginald. *Analytical Experimental Physics.* 2nd rev. ed. Chicago: University of Chicago Press, 1956.

PART THREE

Dunlap, W. M. C. *An Introduction to Semiconductors.* New York: John Wiley & Sons, 1957.

Evans, Joseph. *Fundamental Principles of Transistors.* 2nd ed. Princeton, N.J.: D. Van Nostrand Co., 1962.

Institute of Radio Engineers. *Proceedings.* "Transistor Issue." Nov. 1952.

Jonscher, A. K. *Principles of Semiconductor Device Operation.* New York: John Wiley & Sons, 1960.

Kiver, Milton S. *Transistors in Radio, Television, and Electronics.* 3rd ed. New York: McGraw-Hill Book Co., 1962.

Longini, R. L., and Adler, R. B. *Introduction to Semiconductor Physics.* New York: John Wiley & Sons, 1964.

Sears, F. W. *Principles of Physics.* Vol. 2, *Electricity and Magnetism.* Cambridge, Mass.: Addison-Wesley, 1946.

Shockley, William. *Electrons and Holes in Semiconductors.* Princeton, N.J.: D. Van Nostrand Co., 1950.

Slater, John C. *Modern Physics.* New York: McGraw-Hill Book Co., 1955.

PART FOUR

Bruining, Hajo. *Physics and Applications of Secondary Electron Emission.* New York: Pergamon Press, 1954.

Lytel, Allan Herbert. *ABC's of Lasers and Masers.* Indianapolis: H. W. Sams, 1963. (Paperback.)

Millikan, Robert Andrews. *Electrons (+ and −), Protons, Photons, Neutrons, and Cosmic Rays.* Chicago: University of Chicago Press, 1941.

Troup, Gordon. *Masers.* 2nd ed. New York: John Wiley & Sons, 1963.

Vuylsteke, Arthur A. *Elements of Maser Theory.* Princeton, N.J.: D. Van Nostrand Co., 1960.

Zworykin, Vladimir Kosma, *et al. Electron Optics and the Electron Microscope.* New York: John Wiley & Sons, 1945.

Index

Date Due